PRIVATE PILOT
FLIGHT
MANEUVERS

STEP BY STEP PROCEDURES PLUS PROFILES
BY BRAD DEINES

THIRD EDITION

Dedicated to —
　　　My Father, Jerry Deines

Published by —

**AERO TECH
PUBLICATIONS**

P.O. Box 388
Mansfield, OH 44805

Library of Congress Control Number: 2004195057
Deines, Bradley W.
*Private Pilot Flight Maneuvers —
Step by Step Procedures Plus Profiles*
Third Edition

ISBN 1-886474-05-2 Softcover
ISBN 978-1886474-05-5 Softcover

Cover by Rodney Alling
Cover Photo by Terry Shepherd
Graphics by Lisa Malmquist

Printed in the United States.

"Although the FAA's Practical Test Standards detail the maneuvers and tolerances expected by an examiner during a flight test, they don't explain how the maneuver should be performed. Now a manual from Aero Tech Publications provides 'step by step procedures plus profiles.'"

— FLYING Magazine

"...provide a practical simple carry-along guide for students going after their private license."

— PLANE AND PILOT Magazine

"When it comes to studying the flight maneuvers required for the private certificate there are few, if any, sources that codify and explain them in a step-by-step manner. Until now. Students will know what's expected of them and more importantly, what determines successful completion of the maneuver, before they take wing."

— FLIGHT TRAINING Magazine

"As the FAA recommends, in the Fundamentals of Instruction, the best way to prepare the student to perform a task is to provide a clear, step-by-step example. Private Pilot Flight Maneuvers gives the student recommended patterns to follow and is guaranteed to facilitate learning."

— SEAN JERALDS
Chief Flight Instructor
Embry-Riddle Aeronautical University

"Flight Maneuvers is an easy-to-follow analysis of all required private pilot procedures. Brad's uncomplicated approach is an excellent breakdown for any new pilot, or an effective review for seasoned veterans. A fine reference both in the cockpit or on the ground...a must for any aviation library."

— DAVID ROY
Certified Flight Instructor
Certified Instrument Flight Instructor

TABLE OF CONTENTS

ABOUT THE AUTHOR

Brad Deines. As a boy, Brad first discovered his love for flying accompanying his father on charter flights in a small four seater single engine Cessna. Being only in the fourth grade, Brad was to short to see over the glare shield. So, with a briefcase beneath him to see out the windshield, the charter pilot gave him his first flying lesson. Takeoffs, climbs, cruise, descents, and landings, Brad did it all. You could not pry the smile off his face for weeks afterwards. It was shortly thereafter, he knew aviation would play a major role in his life.

Using his own money saved from working odd jobs, he began taking flying lessons when he was 16 years old at a local flight school in Casper, Wyoming. As with most pilots, he recalls vividly the first time he soloed. Not really knowing he was going to solo that day, his instructor told him to park the aircraft at the base of the control tower. After Brad shut the engine down, he wondered why his instructor had him park here. With a quick signature in Brad's logbook, the instructor jumped out and Brad was off on his own to do three takeoff and landings. To this day he still remembers shouting at the top of his lungs "YAHOOO!" as he flew his first downwind leg by himself.

He finished getting his Private Pilot's Certificate at the fixed base operator in Casper with just minimum flight time. As a matter of fact, the morning of his checkride, he had to fly a cross country as part of his minimum requirements. Even after he did that, he had to stay in the practice area doing maneuvers until he had the minimum 40 hours required by the Federal Aviation Administration.

To continue his flying education, he then applied and was accepted to attend Embry-Riddle Aeronautical University in Prescott, Arizona. A University known as the "Harvard of the Sky", where every subject Brad took had some connection to aviation. After four years, he left with a Bachelor of Science Degree in Aeronautical Science and a Commercial Multiengine Certificate with Instrument Privileges.

He then acquired his flight instructor ratings at a flight school located at Sky Harbor airport in Phoenix, Arizona. With a CFI and CFII in his hands now, he began giving instruction. He spent several years as a flight instructor and ground instructor. He then returned to his almamater to become a flight manager for Embry-Riddle teaching all levels of flight training. This included basic levels to the Boeing 737 simulator training program. Brad was also a certified check airman for Embry-Riddle Aeronautical University where he administered check rides for students testing for their Private Pilot Certificate, Commercial Pilot Certificate, Instrument Pilot Rating and Multi-engine license.

It was during this entire time as a flight instructor that he spent two years researching and writing this manual for his students. He wanted to give his students a comprehensive, professional manual covering all the flight maneuvers required to fly an airplane safely and efficiently.

Today, Brad is a captain for a major airline where he applies the procedures described in this manual on almost a daily basis.

Brad is the owner of Aero Tech Publications, a company which has specialized in aviation publications for over 10 years. He is also the author of:

Commercial Pilot Flight Maneuvers — Step by Step Procedures Plus Profiles.

Instrument Pilot Flight Maneuvers — Step by Step Procedures Plus Profiles.

Multi-Engine Pilot Flight Maneuvers — Step by Step Procedures Plus Profiles.

PREFACE

The purpose of this manual is to help in the explanation, visualization and execution of the flight maneuvers required for Private Pilot Practical Flight Test. Students preparing for their Private Pilot Certificate will find this manual helpful. Any pilot preparing for a Biennial Flight Review (BFR), can use this manual as a refresher on maneuvers that you may not have executed in quite some time. Flight Instructor applicants and Flight Instructors will find this manual a beneficial teaching aid. Instructors and flight schools can use this manual to develop thorough and standardized lesson plans.

Each maneuver is broken into six sections.

1. **Objective** — the Federal Aviation Administration's goal for a pilot as stated in the practical test standards.

2. **Completion Standards** — are taken from the Private Pilot Practical Test Standards. This details exactly what the Federal Aviation Administration requests of a pilot executing a maneuver. The limitations listed are the tolerances allowed on a Federal Aviation Administration's check ride. If these standards are not met, you will not pass your check ride.

3. **Description** — a brief explanation of the maneuver.

4. **Procedure** — a detailed step by step explanation of how to execute a maneuver as recommended by the Federal Aviation Administration. Each maneuver may vary slightly due to airplane type, manufacturer's recommendations, training environment and level. A Certified Flight Instructor will provide guidance on how the maneuver should vary for your particular situation.

5. **Reference** — contains the Federal Aviation Administration's Advisory Circulars (AC's) on which the previous sections are based. Page numbers are listed for location of additional information and easy reference on each flight maneuver. Since the FAA, or their designee, is the one testing you, it only makes sense to use the references they have based the test on and not other authors/publishers books. The FAA books can be downloaded for free at the FAA Standards web site http://av-info.faa.gov.

6. **Profiles** — most maneuvers also contain a graphic representation(s) of each maneuver. This graphic assists in visualizing the maneuver while summarizing the procedures and

completion standards. On most profile pages you will have a table where you can fill in your particular aircraft airspeeds, pitch attitudes, bank angles, power settings and configurations.

All airspeeds, pitch attitudes, bank angles, power settings and configurations are referenced from the 1984 Cessna 172P Pilot's Operating Handbook based on sea level, maximum gross weight, and standard atmospheric conditions. Airspeeds, pitch attitudes, bank angles and power settings may vary due to altitude, temperature, humidity, winds, aircraft weight and configurations. Consult your airplane Pilot's Operating Handbook and/or your flight instructor for the proper airspeeds, pitch attitudes, bank angles, power settings and configurations.

HOW TO USE THIS MANUAL

Before every flight lesson, know exactly what flight maneuvers will be practiced. Reference your flight syllabus for the maneuvers to study. Divide the list into two sections: **New Maneuvers** for the maneuvers your instructor is going to introduce or teach for the first time; and **Review Maneuvers,** for maneuvers you are familiar with but will be practicing on your next flight lesson.

New Maneuvers — Start by reading the maneuver's six sections. If there are questions on a particular step in the maneuver, reference the appropriate Federal Aviation Administration Advisory Circular or other references listed for each maneuver. If an answer cannot be found, write it down and ask your instructor during the pre-flight briefing. Go over the procedure section several times until you every step memorized. Practice the maneuver by "chair flying" the step by step procedure. (Chair Flying - visually flying the maneuver in your comfortable chair at home). By doing all this preparation, you will impress your flight instructor with your knowledge and understanding of the maneuver before you even step into an airplane. Not to mention the money you will save in less dual flying time.

Review Maneuvers — The profile section in most cases will continue to refresh your memory on the steps required to complete the maneuver. If it has been several weeks since practicing this maneuver, it may be best to follow the steps listed for a new maneuver. Continue to "chair fly" the maneuver on your off days to maintain your proficiency.

CHAPTER ONE
ORAL SUBJECTS

CERTIFICATES AND DOCUMENTS

OBJECTIVE AND COMPLETION STANDARDS

1. To teach the private pilot student the knowledge of the elements related to certificates and documents such as:
   a. private pilot certificate privileges, limitations, and recent flight experience requirements.
   b. medical certificate class and duration.
   c. pilot logbook or flight records.
2. To be able to locate and explain the following:
   a. airworthiness and registration certificates.
   b. operating limitations, placards, instrument markings and POH/AFM.
   c. weight and balance data and equipment list.

References
Private Pilot Practical Test Standards FAA-S-8081-14A, pg. 1-1.
Federal Aviation Regulations, 43, 61.1 ⇒ 61.5, 61.13, 61.15 ⇒ 61.17, 61.23 ⇒ 61.60, 61.102 ⇒ 61.117, 91.1 ⇒ 91.25.
Airplane Flying Handbook FAA-H-8083-3, pg. 2.1.
Pilot's Handbook of Aeronautical Knowledge AC61-23/FAA-H-8083-25, pg. 7.1 ⇒ 7.7

AIRWORTHINESS REQUIREMENTS

OBJECTIVE AND COMPLETION STANDARDS

1. To teach the private pilot student the knowledge of the elements related to airworthiness requirements such as:
   a. required instruments and equipment for day/night VFR.
   b. procedures and limitations for determining airworthiness of the airplane with inoperative instruments and equipment with and without an MEL.
   c. requirements and procedures for obtaining a special flight permit.
2. To be able to locate and explain the following:
   a. airworthiness directives.
   b. compliance records.
   c. maintenance/inspection requirements.
   d. appropriate record keeping.

References
Private Pilot Practical Test Standards FAA-S-8081-14A, pg. 1-1
Federal Aviation Regulations, 91.151 ⇒ 91.145, 91.201 ⇒ 91.421.
Pilot's Handbook of Aeronautical Knowledge AC61-23/FAA-H-8083-25, 7.7 ⇒ 7-11.

WEATHER INFORMATION

OBJECTIVE AND COMPLETION STANDARDS

1. To teach the private pilot student the knowledge of the elements related to weather information by analyzing weather reports, charts, and forecasts from various sources with emphasis on:
   a. METAR, TAF, and FA.
   b. surface analysis chart.
   c. radar summary chart.
   d. winds and temperature aloft chart.
   e. significant weather prognostic charts.
   f. convective outlook chart.
   g. AWOS, ASOS, and ATIS reports.

2. To be able to make a competent "go/no go" decision based on available weather information.

References

Private Pilot Practical Test Standards FAA-S-8081-14A, pg. 1-2.
Federal Aviation Regulations Part 91.151 ⇒ 91.159.
Aviation Weather AC 00-6.
Aviation Weather Services AC 00-45.
Pilot's Handbook of Aeronautical Knowledge AC61-23/FAA-H-8083-25, pg. 10-1 ⇒ 11-19.
Role of Preflight Preparation AC 61-84.
Aeronautical Information Manual, para. 7-1-1 ⇒ 7-1-53.

CROSS-COUNTRY FLIGHT PLANNING

OBJECTIVE AND COMPLETION STANDARDS

1. To teach the private pilot student the knowledge of the elements related to cross-country flight planning by presenting and explaining a pre-planned VFR cross-country flight, as previously assigned by the examiner. On the day of the practical test, the final flight plan shall be to the first fuel stop, based on maximum allowable passengers, baggage, and/or cargo loads using real-time weather.

2. Uses appropriate and current aeronautical charts.

3. Properly identifies airspace, obstructions, and terrain features.

4 Selects easily identifiable en route checkpoints.

5. Selects most favorable altitudes considering weather conditions and equipment capabilities.

6. Computes headings, flight time, and fuel requirements.

7. Selects appropriate navigation system/facilities and communication frequencies.

8. Applies pertinent information from NOTAMs, AF/D, and other flight publications.

9. Completes a navigation log and simulates filing a VFR flight plan.

References
Private Pilot Practical Test Standards FAA-S-8081-14A, pg. 1-2.
Federal Aviation Regulations, Part 91.103, 91.119, 91.121, 91.151 ⇒ 91.159.
Pilots Handbook of Aeronautical Knowledge AC 61-23/FAA-H-8083-25, pg. 14-1 ⇒ 14-28.
Role of Preflight Preparation AC 61-84.
Aeronautical Information Manual, para 3-1-4, 3-1-5, 5-1-1 ⇒ 5-1-5, 5-1-9 ⇒ 5-1-12, 7-2-1 ⇒ 7-2-2, 7-4-6, 9-1-1 ⇒ 9-1-4.
Navigational Charts and AF/D

NATIONAL AIRSPACE SYSTEM

OBJECTIVE AND COMPLETION STANDARDS
1. To teach the private pilot student the knowledge of the elements related to the National Airspace System such as:
   a. Basic VFR weather minimums - for all classes of airspace.
   b. Airspace classes - their operating rules, pilot certification, and airplane equipment requirements for the following:
      1. Class A.
      2. Class B.
      3. Class C
      4. Class D
      5. Class E
      6. Class G.
   c. Special use and other airspace areas.

References
Private Pilot Practical Test Standards FAA-S-8081-14A, pg. 1-3.
Federal Aviation Regulations, part 71, 91.126 ⇒ 91.145, 91.155, 91.157.
Aeronautical Information Manual, para. 3-1-1 ⇒ 3-5-7.
Navigation Charts.

PERFORMANCE AND LIMITATIONS

OBJECTIVE AND COMPLETION STANDARDS

1. To teach the private pilot student the knowledge of the elements related to performance and limitations with the use of charts, tables, and data to determine performance and the adverse effects of exceeding limitations.

2. Compute weight and balance. Determine the computed weight and center of gravity is within the airplane's operating limitations and if the weight and center of gravity will remain within limits during all phases of flight.

3. Demonstrate use of the appropriate charts, tables, and data.

4. Describe the effects of atmospheric conditions on the airplane's performance.

References
Private Pilot Practical Test Standards FAA-S-8081-14A, pg. 1-3.
Pilot's Handbook of Aeronautical Knowledge AC 61-23, FAA-H-8083-25, pg. 8-1 ⇒ 9-60.
Aircraft Weight and Balance FAA-H-8083-1.
Role of Preflight Preparation AC 61-84.
Pilot Operating Handbook/Approved Flight Manual.

OPERATION OF SYSTEMS

OBJECTIVE AND COMPLETION STANDARDS

1. To teach the private pilot student the knowledge of the elements related to the elements related to the operation of systems on the airplane provided for the flight test by explaining at least three (3) of the following systems:
   a. Primary flight controls.
   b. Flaps, leading edge devices, and spoilers.
   c. Powerplant and propeller.
   d. Landing gear.
   e. Fuel, oil, and hydraulic.
   f. Electrical.
   g. Avionics.
   h. Pitot-static vacuum/pressure and associated flight instruments.
   i. Environmental.
   j. Deicing and anti-icing.

References
Private Pilot Practical Test Standards FAA-S-8081-14A, pg. 1-4.
Pilots Handbook of Aeronautical Knowledge AC 61-23/FAA-H-8083-25,
pg. 4-1 ⇒ 6-17
Pilot Operating Handbook/Approved Flight Manual.

AEROMEDICAL FACTORS

OBJECTIVE AND COMPLETION STANDARDS

1. To teach the private pilot student the knowledge of the elements related to aeromedical factors by explaining:the symptoms, causes, effects, and corrective actions of at least three (3) of the following:
   a. hypoxia.
   b. hyperventilation.
   c. middle ear and sinus problems.
   d. spatial disorientation.
   e. motion sickness.
   f. carbon monoxide poisoning.
   g. Stress and fatigue.
   h. dehydration.

2. The effects of alcohol, drugs, and over-the-counter medications.

3. The effects of excesses nitrogen during scuba dives upon a pilot or passenger in flight.

References
Private Pilot Practical Test Standards FAA-S-8081-14A, pg. 1-5.
Pilot's Handbook of Aeronautical Knowledge AC 61-23/FAA-H-8083-25,
pg. 15-1 ⇒ 15-12.
Aeronautical Information Manual, para. 8-1-1 ⇒ 8-1-8.

PREFLIGHT INSPECTION

OBJECTIVE AND COMPLETION STANDARDS

1. To teach the private pilot student the knowledge of the elements related to preflight inspection. This shall include which items must be inspected, the reasons for checking each item, and how to detect possible defects.

2. Inspect the airplane with reference to an appropriate checklist.

3. Verify the airplane is in condition for safe flight.

References
Private Pilot Practical Test Standards FAA-S-8081-14A, pg. 1-6.
Airplane Flying Handbook FAA-H-8083-3, pg. 2-1 ⇒ 2-6.
Pilot Operating Handbook/Approved Flight Manual.

COCKPIT MANAGEMENT

OBJECTIVE AND COMPLETION STANDARDS

1. To teach the private pilot student the knowledge of the elements related to cockpit management procedures.

2. Ensure all loose items in the cockpit and cabin are secured.

3. Organize material and equipment in an efficient manner so they are readily available.

4. Brief occupants on the use of safety belts, shoulder harnesses, doors, and emergency procedures.

References
Private Pilot Practical Test Standards FAA-S-8081-14A, pg. 1-6.
Airplane Flying Handbook FAA-H-8083-3, pg. 2-7.
Pilot Operating Handbook/Approved Flight Manual.

RADIO COMMUNICATIONS AND ATC LIGHT SIGNALS

OBJECTIVE AND COMPLETION STANDARDS

1. To teach the private pilot student the knowledge of the elements related to radio communications and ATC light signals.

2. Selects appropriate frequencies.

3. Transmits using recommended phraseology.

4. Acknowledges radio communications and complies with instructions.

References
Private Pilot Practical Test Standards FAA-S-8081-14A, pg. 1-9.
Federal Aviation Regulations, part 91.123, 91.125.
Pilot's Handbook of Aeronautical Knowledge AC-61-23/FAA-H-8083-25, pg. 12-1, 12-2, 12-8 ⇒ 12-12.
Aeronautical Information Manual, para. 4-1-1 ⇒ 4-4-15, 6-4-1.

AIRPORT, RUNWAY, AND TAXIWAY SIGNS, MARKINGS AND LIGHTING

OBJECTIVE AND COMPLETION STANDARDS

1. To teach the private pilot student the knowledge of the elements related to airport, runway, and taxiway operations with emphasis on runway incursion avoidance.

2. Properly identifies and interprets airport, runway, and taxiway signs, markings, and lighting.

References
Private Pilot Practical Test Standards FAA-S-8081-14A, pg. 1-9.
Pilot's Handbook of Aeronautical Knowledge AC 61-23/FAA-H-8083-25, pg. 12-3 ⇒ 12-8.
Aeronautical Information Manual, para. 2-1-1 ⇒ 2-3-14.

PILOTAGE AND DEAD RECKONING

OBJECTIVE AND COMPLETION STANDARDS

1. To teach the private pilot student the knowledge of the elements related to pilotage and dead reckoning.

2. Follows the preplanned course by reference to landmarks.

3. Identifies landmarks by relating surface features to chart symbols.

4. Navigates by means of precomputed headings, groundspeeds, and elapsed time.

5. Corrects for and records the differences between preflight groundspeed and heading calculations and those determined en route.

6. Verifies the airplane's position within three (3) nautical miles of the flight-planned route.

7. Arrives at the enroute checkpoints within five (5) minutes of the initial or revised ETA and provides a destination estimate.

8. Maintains the appropriate altitude, ±200 feet (60 meters) and headings, ±15°.

References
Private Pilot Practical Test Standards FAA-S-8081-14A, pg. 1-24.
Pilot's Handbook of Aeronautical Knowledge AC 61-23/FAA-H-8083-25, pg. 14-10 ⇒ 14-12.

SPIN AWARENESS

OBJECTIVE AND COMPLETION STANDARDS

1. To teach the private pilot student the knowledge of the elements related to spin awareness.

2. Explain the aerodynamic factors related to spins.

3. Explain flight situations where unintentional spins may occur.

4. Explain procedures for recovery from unintentional spins.

References

Private Pilot Practical Test Standards FAA-S-8081-14A, pg. 1-28.
Airplane Flying Handbook FAA-H-8083-3, pg. 4-12 ⇒ 4-16.
Stall and Spin Awareness Training AC 61-67.
Pilot Operating Handbook/Approved Flight Manual.

RADIO COMMUNICATIONS, NAVIGATION SYSTEM/FACILITIES, AND RADAR SERVICES

OBJECTIVE AND COMPLETION STANDARDS

1. To teach the private pilot student the knowledge of the elements related to radio communications, navigation system/facilities, and radar services.

2. Selects the proper frequency and identifies the appropriate facility.

3. Follows verbal instructions and/or navigation systems/facilities for guidance.

4. Determines the minimum safe altitude.

5. Maintains altitude, ±200 feet (60 meters); maintains heading, ±20°; maintains airspeed, ±10 knots.

References

Private Pilot Practical Test Standards FAA-S-8081-14A, pg. 1-28.
Pilot's Handbook of Aeronautical Knowledge AC 61-23/FAA-H-8083-25, pg. 12-10, 12-11.
Instrument Flying Handbook FAA-H-8083-15, pg. 9-1 ⇒ 9-12.

SYSTEMS AND EQUIPMENT MALFUNCTIONS

OBJECTIVE AND COMPLETION STANDARDS

1. To teach the private pilot student the knowledge of the elements related to system and equipment malfunctions appropriate to the airplane provided for the practical test.

2. Analyzes the situation and takes appropriate action for simulated emergencies appropriate to the airplane provided for the practical test for at least three (3) of the following:
   a. partial or complete power loss.
   b. engine roughness or overheat.
   c. carburetor or induction icing.
   d. loss of oil pressure.
   e. fuel starvation.
   f. electrical malfunction.
   g. vacuum/pressure, and associated flight instruments malfunction.
   h. pitot/static.
   i. landing gear or flap malfunction.
   j. inoperative trim.
   k. inadvertent door or window opening.
   l. structural icing.
   m. smoke/fire/engine compartment fire.
   n. any other emergency appropriate to the airplane.

3. Follows the appropriate checklist or procedure.

Reference
Private Pilot Practical Test Standards FAA-S-8081-14A, pg. 1-33.
Airplane Flying Handbook FAA-H-8083-3, pg. 16-1 ⇒ 16-12.
Pilot Operating Handbook/Approved Flight Manual

EMERGENCY EQUIPMENT AND SURVIVAL GEAR

OBJECTIVE AND COMPLETION STANDARDS

1. To teach the private pilot student the knowledge of the elements related to emergency equipment and survival gear appropriate to the airplane and environment encountered during flight. Identifies appropriate equipment that should be aboard the airplane.

References
Private Pilot Practical Test Standards FAA-S-8081-14A, pg. 1-33.
Airplane Flying Handbook FAA-H-8083-3.
Pilot Operating Handbook/Approved Flight Manual.

NIGHT PREPARATION

OBJECTIVE AND COMPLETION STANDARDS

1. To teach the private pilot student the knowledge of the elements related to night operations to include:
   a. Physiological aspects of night flying as it relates to vision.
   b. Lighting systems identifying airports, runways, taxiways, and obstructions, and pilot controlled lighting.
   c. Airplane lighting systems.
   d. Personal equipment essential for night flight.
   e. Night orientation, navigation, and chart reading techniques.
   f. Safety precautions and emergencies unique to night flying.

References
Private Pilot Practical Test Standards FAA-S-8081-14A, pg. 1-34.
Airplane Flying Handbook FAA-H-8083-3, pg. 10-1 ⇒ 10-8
Pilot's Handbook of Aeronautical Knowledge AC 61-23/FAA-H-8083-25, pg. 15-10 ⇒ 15-12.
Medical Handbook for Pilots AC 67-2, pg. 8 ⇒ 10.
Aeronautical Information Manual, para. 2-1-1 ⇒ 2-2-3.
Pilot Operating Handbook/Approved Flight Manual.

CHAPTER TWO
PREFLIGHT PROCEDURES

ENGINE STARTING

OBJECTIVE

To teach the private pilot student the knowledge of the elements related to engine starting procedures. This shall include the use of an external power source, hand propping safety, and starting under various atmospheric conditions.

COMPLETION STANDARDS

1. Position the airplane properly considering structures, surface conditions, other aircraft, and the safety of nearby persons and property.
2. Utilize the appropriate checklist for starting procedure.

DESCRIPTION

After before starting checklists are complete, a safe check around the airplane and propeller is made. Normal engine starting sequence is then started.

PROCEDURE

1. Complete preflight and cockpit setup. During preflight consider which way the airplane is pointed so as not to blast any dirt on or knock over any objects or people behind you.
2. Complete before starting checklist.
3. Verify parking brake is set. In addition, put feet on brakes just in case the parking brake does fail.
4. Turn beacon on.
5. Shout "PROP CLEAR" outside the window.
6. Verify no persons or objects are in vicinity of the propeller.
7. Conduct normal start per Pilot's Operating Handbook/Approved Flight Manual.
8. Verify oil pressure after the engine has started. If not, shut the engine down.
9. Verify the starter has disengaged by checking for large draw on electrical system or by a warning light as installed. If still engaged, shut the engine down.
10. Complete after start checklist.

References

Private Pilot Practical Test Standards FAA-S-8081-14A, pg. 1-6.
Airplane Flying Handbook FA-H-8083-3, pg. 2-7 ⇒ 2-9.
Pilot's Handbook of Aeronautical Knowledge AC 61-23/FAA-H-8083-25, pg. 5-16.
Cold Weather Operation of Aircraft AC 91-13C.
Reduction of Electrical System Failures Following Aircraft Engine Starting AC 91-55.
Pilot Operating Handbook/Approved Flight Manual.

TAXIING

OBJECTIVE

To teach the private pilot student the knowledge of the elements related to safe taxi procedures.

COMPLETION STANDARDS

1. Performs a brake check immediately after the airplane begins moving.
2. Positions the flight controls properly for the existing wind conditions.
3. Controls direction and speed without excessive use of brakes.
4. Complies with airport/taxi markings, signals, ATC clearances and instructions.
5. Taxies so as to avoid other aircraft and hazards.

DESCRIPTION

Movement of the aircraft under it's own power around the airport in a safe manner considering other traffic, obstacles, weather and wind. Complies with ATC clearances and airport markings.

PROCEDURE

1. Complete the after engine start checklist.
2. Obtain taxi clearance from ATC or state intentions over the radio at an uncontrolled airport.
3. Look all around the aircraft for any other aircraft, obstacle or debris that could possibly be in conflict with your taxiing or damage the aircraft.
4. Release the parking brake.
5. Add just enough power to get the airplane rolling.
6. Reduce power back to idle.
7. Check braking system for normal operation.
8. Continue taxiing following ATC instructions or making position reports if at an uncontrolled airport.
9. Position flight controls appropriately for the existing wind conditions.

a. Headwind - Up and Into - turn the ailerons into the wind so the upwind aileron is deflected up and the elevator is neutral or slightly up.

b. Tailwind - Down and Away - turn the ailerons away from the wind so the upwind aileron is down and the elevator is also down.

c. After each turn on a taxiway recheck the position of the flight controls as the wind has shifted to a new position on the aircraft.

10. Maintain a safe taxi speed. Be able to stop the aircraft promptly if necessary. Maintain slower taxi speeds on ramps, congested areas and with contaminated surfaces.

11. When necessary to slow the airplane, first reduce power to idle then, if necessary, apply braking.

12. In making turns, use full rudder deflection first and then if necessary use differential braking in decrease the radius of the turn.

13. Once clear of congested/ramp area, perform instrument cockpit check. Divide attention between taxing the aircraft and doing your instrument checks. If taxing at a busy airport, reduced visibility or on contaminated surfaces, do all but your turning instrument checks while stopped with the parking brake set.

a. Magnetic compass bowl full of fluid, no bubbles; heading card on inside moves freely; check against a known heading (taxiways/runways); deviation card installed.

b. Clock — set to current time and check operation.

c. Airspeed indicator — check on zero.

d. Heading indicator — set to magnetic compass after allowing a 5 minute warm up period.

e. Suction/Gyro pressure — check pressure.

f. After allowing a 5 minute warm up period, check the gyro instruments while making turns to the left and to the right:
1. Attitude indicator — Set miniature airplane to level flight. No more than five degrees bank precession. No abnormal vibrations.
2. Turn coordinator — proper turn indications. The airplane or needle turns in the same direction of the turn. The ball moves freely and moves opposite the direction of turn.
3. Heading indicator — turns in proper direction.

g. Altimeter — set current altimeter setting, maximum error ± 75 feet from known field elevation. If no altimeter setting is available then set the altimeter to the known field elevation.

h. Vertical speed indicator — should indicate zero. Note any error or adjust to zero if able.

i. Engine instruments — check for normal readings.
j. Circuit breakers — check in.
k. Alternate static source — check normal position.
l. De-icing/Anti-icing equipment — check operation.
m. Do normal engine runup including to check carburetor heat.
n. Preflight any other anti/deice systems.

Note: The sequence in which the flight instruments, communication, navigational and anti-icing/de-icing equipment are checked can be modified to establish a logical flow for the particular airplane being used.

References
Private Pilot Practical Test Standards FA-S-8081-14A, pg. 1-7.
Airplane Flying Handbook FAA-H-8083-3, pg. 2-9 ⇒ 2-11.
Pilots Operating Handbook/Approved Flight Manual.
Instrument Flying Handbook FAA-H-8083-15, pg. 3-23 ⇒3-24.
Aeronautical Information Manual, para. 1-1-1, 7-2-3.
Federal Aviation Regulation's 91.121, 91.171, 91.205(d).

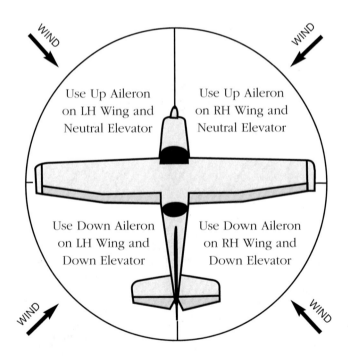

BEFORE TAKEOFF CHECK

OBJECTIVE

To teach the private pilot student the knowledge of the elements related to the before takeoff check. This shall include reasons for checking each item and how to detect malfunctions.

COMPLETION STANDARDS

1. Positions the airplane properly considering other aircraft, wind and surface conditions.
2. Divides attention inside and outside the cockpit.
3. Ensures that engine temperature and pressure are suitable for runup and takeoff.
4. Accomplishes the before takeoff checklist and ensures the airplane is in safe operating condition.
5. Reviews takeoff performance airspeeds, takeoff distances, departure, and emergency procedures.
6. Avoids runway incursions and/or ensures no conflict with traffic prior to taxiing into takeoff position.

DESCRIPTION

An engine, systems, controls, instruments and avionics check after the engine has reached minimum operating temperature and before takeoff.

PROCEDURE

1. Position the aircraft in the runup area taking into the following considerations:
   a. Clear of other aircraft.
   b. Nothing behind the aircraft that could cause damage due to prop blast.
   c. Firm surface to prevent blowing debris and prop damage.
   d. Nose of aircraft pointed into the wind to provide cooling.
2. Straighten nose wheel by rolling forward slightly.
3. Set parking brake.
4. Verify engine has reached minimum operating temperatures.
5. Conduct engine runup per pilot's operating handbook/approved flight manual.

6. Divide attention between inside and outside the aircraft paying particular attention to if the airplane begins to roll due to the parking brake slipping.

7. Complete the before takeoff checklist.

8. Review performance data for the runway and departure path.

9. Consider emergency procedures for the departure runway.

References

Private Pilot Practical Test Standards FAA-S-8081-14A, pg. 1-8.
Airplane Flying Handbook FAA-H-8083-3, pg. 2-11.
Pilot Operating Handbook/Approved Flight Manual.

CHAPTER THREE
TAKEOFFS, LANDINGS, GO-AROUNDS, AND TRAFFIC PATTERN OPERATIONS

....

NORMAL TAKEOFF AND CLIMB

OBJECTIVE

To teach the private student the knowledge of the elements related to a normal takeoff, climb operations, and rejected takeoff procedures.

COMPLETION STANDARDS

1. Positions the flight controls for existing wind conditions.
2. Clears the area; taxies into the takeoff position and aligns the airplane on the runway center/takeoff path.
3. Lifts off at the recommended airspeed and accelerates to V_Y.
4. Establishes a pitch attitude that will maintain V_Y +10/-5 knots.
5. Retracts the landing gear, if appropriate, and flaps after a positive rate of climb is established.
6. Maintains takeoff power and V_Y +10/-5 knots to a safe maneuvering altitude.
7. Maintains directional control and proper wind-drift correction throughout the takeoff and climb.
8. Complies with noise abatement procedures.
9. Completes the appropriate checklist.

DESCRIPTION

The airplane will be aligned with runway centerline. Takeoff power will be applied smoothly, instruments will be checked and the airplane allowed to accelerate to rotation speed, then the pitch attitude is increased to establish a climb out at V_Y airspeed.

PROCEDURE

1. Set recommended flaps.
2. Clear final approach.
3. After receiving clearance from tower or announcing intentions on the common traffic advisory frequency, taxi onto the runway.
4. Align the airplane on the runway centerline.
5. Advance the throttle smoothly to maximum allowable power.
6. Check the engine instruments.

7. Check airspeed alive.

8. Maintain directional control on runway centerline by use of the rudder. Avoid using brakes.

9. Rotate smoothly at V_R and establish the pitch attitude for V_Y.

10. If a significant headwind or gusty wind conditions exist, the airplane should be held on the ground slightly longer than normal so a smooth and definite lift off can be made.

11. Keep the wings level with use of the ailerons.

12. Retract the wing flaps when at a safe speed and safe altitude (minimum 50 feet AGL).

13. Accelerate and maintain V_Y.

14. Retract landing gear after positive rate of climb and a safe landing can no longer be accomplished on the remaining runway.

15. Maintain takeoff power and V_Y to 500 feet AGL or until all obstacles are cleared.

16. Accelerate to cruise climb airspeed then set climb power.

17. Maintain a straight track over the extended runway centerline until a turn is required.

18. Avoid noise sensitive areas.

19. Complete after-takeoff checklist.

Note: FAR 91.103 requires takeoff and landing performance data to be computed prior to all flights.

References
Private Pilot Practical Test Standards FAA-S-8081-14A, pg. 1-10.
Airplane Flying Handbook FAA-H-8083-3, pg. 5-1 $\Rightarrow$ 5-5.

CROSSWIND TAKEOFF AND CLIMB

OBJECTIVE

To teach the private student the knowledge of the elements related to a crosswind takeoff and climb.

COMPLETION STANDARDS

1. Positions the flight controls for existing wind conditions.
2. Clears the area; taxies into the takeoff position and aligns the airplane on the runway center/takeoff path.
3. Lifts off at the recommended airspeed and accelerates to V_Y.
4. Establishes a pitch attitude that will maintain V_Y +10/-5 knots.
5. Retracts the landing gear, if appropriate, and flaps after a positive rate of climb is established.
6. Maintains takeoff power and V_Y +10/-5 knots to a safe maneuvering altitude.
7. Maintains directional control and proper wind-drift correction throughout the takeoff and climb.
8. Complies with noise abatement procedures.
9. Completes the appropriate checklist.

DESCRIPTION

Aileron will be held into the wind to correct for drift, and rudder will be used to maintain runway alignment during the takeoff roll. Once airborne, a wind-drift correction will be established to maintain a ground track alignment with the runway centerline.

PROCEDURE

1. Set recommended flaps.
2. Clear final approach.
3. After receiving clearance from tower or announcing intentions on the common traffic advisory frequency, taxi onto the runway
4. Align the airplane on the runway centerline, ailerons fully deflected into the wind, and elevator in the neutral position.
5. Smoothly apply full power and crosscheck the engine instruments.

5. Check airspeed alive.

6. As the airplane accelerates, adjust the ailerons as necessary to control drift and maintain runway alignment with the rudder. Avoid using brakes.

7. If a significant crosswind and/or strong gusts exist, the airplane should be held on the ground slightly longer than normal (past V_R) so a smooth and definite lift off can be made.

8. As the airplane leaves the runway, holding the aileron into the wind may result in the downwind wing rising and downwind main wheel lifting off first. This is acceptable, and prevents airplane from skipping across the runway.

9. Once the airplane lifts off, relax the control inputs to help establish wind drift correction.

10. Continue tracking along the extended centerline and establish the proper climb attitude for existing conditions.

11. Retract the wing flaps when at safe altitude (minimum 50 feet AGL) and at a safe altitude .

12. Accelerate and maintain V_Y.

13. Retract landing gear after positive rate of climb and a safe landing can no longer be accomplished on the remaining runway.

14. Maintain takeoff power to 500 feet AGL.

15. Accelerate to cruise climb airspeed and set climb power.

16. Avoid noise sensitive areas.

17. Complete after-takeoff checklist.

Note: FAR 91.103 requires takeoff and landing performance data be computed prior to all flights.

References
Private Pilot Practical Test Standards FAA-S-8081-14A, pg. 1-10.
Airplane Flying Handbook FAA-H-8083-3, pg. 5-5 $\Rightarrow$ 5-7.

NORMAL/CROSSWIND TAKE-OFF

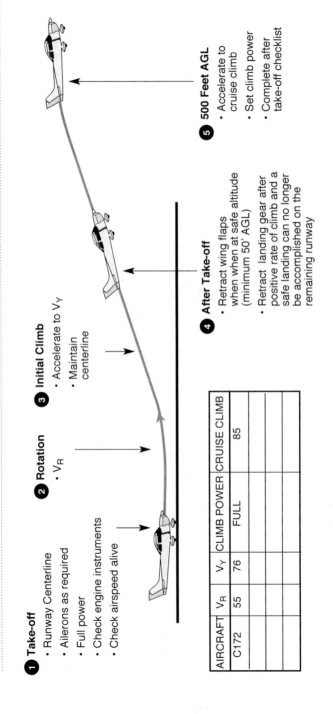

1 Take-off
- Runway Centerline
- Ailerons as required
- Full power
- Check engine instruments
- Check airspeed alive

2 Rotation
- V_R

3 Initial Climb
- Accelerate to V_Y
- Maintain centerline

4 After Take-off
- Retract wing flaps when when at safe altitude (minimum 50' AGL)
- Retract landing gear after positive rate of climb and a safe landing can no longer be accomplished on the remaining runway

5 500 Feet AGL
- Accelerate to cruise climb
- Set climb power
- Complete after take-off checklist

AIRCRAFT	V_R	V_Y	CLIMB POWER	CRUISE CLIMB
C172	55	76	FULL	85

Limitations — V_Y +10/-5 Knots

SHORT-FIELD TAKEOFF AND MAXIMUM PERFORMANCE CLIMB

OBJECTIVE

To teach the private student the knowledge of the elements related to a short-field takeoff and maximum performance climb.

COMPLETION STANDARDS

1. Positions the flight controls for the existing wind conditions; sets flaps as recommended.
2. Clears the area; taxies into the takeoff position utilizing maximum available takeoff area and aligns the airplane on the runway center/takeoff path.
3. Applies brakes (if appropriate), while advancing the throttle smoothly to takeoff power.
4. Lifts off at the recommended airspeed, and accelerates to the recommended obstacle clearance airspeed or V_X.
5. Establishes the pitch attitude that will maintain the recommended obstacle clearance airspeed, or V_X, +10/-5 knots, until the obstacle is cleared, or until the airplane is 50 feet (20 meters) above the surface.
6. After clearing the obstacle, establishes the pitch attitude for V_Y, accelerates to V_Y, and maintains V_Y, +10/-5 knots, during the climb.
7. Retracts the landing gear, if appropriate, and flaps after clear of any obstacles or as recommended by manufacturer.
8. Maintains takeoff power and V_Y +10/-5 to a safe maneuvering altitude.
9. Maintains directional control and proper wind-drift correction throughout the takeoff and climb.
10. Completes the appropriate checklist.

DESCRIPTION

The airplane is accelerated in the shortest distance possible, rotated at lift off speed to the best angle of climb so as to minimize total takeoff distance and/or clear an obstacle.

PROCEDURE

1. Set flaps to recommended setting.

2. Clear final approach.

3. After receiving clearance from tower or announcing intentions on the common traffic advisory frequency, taxi into position at the end of the runway so that maximum runway is available for takeoff.

4. Set flight controls for the existing winds.

5. Hold brakes and smoothly add maximum power.

6. Lean mixture for maximum power.

7. Check engine instruments and static power.

8. Release brakes.

9. Check airspeed alive.

10. Maintain runway centerline by use of the rudder, avoid using brakes.

11. Rotate at computed V_R for airplane weight.

12. Set V_X attitude and accelerate to V_X for appropriate airplane weight.

13. Keep the wings level with use of the ailerons.

14. Climb at V_X until obstacle is cleared or until at least 50 feet above the surface, set pitch for V_Y.

15. Retract landing gear as recommended in the Pilot's Operating Handbook/Approved Fight Manual. (POH/.AFM).

16. Retract the wing flaps when at a safe altitude (minimum 50 feet AGL) and at safe speed.

17. Accelerate and maintain V_Y.

18. Maintain takeoff power to 500 feet AGL or safe maneuvering altitude.

19. Ensure that airplane tracks out on the extended centerline until turn is required.

20. Accelerate to cruise climb airspeed and set climb power.

21. Avoid noise sensitive areas.

22. Complete after-takeoff checklist.

Note: FAR 91.103 requires takeoff and landing performance data to be computed prior to all flights.

References
Private Pilot Practical Test Standards FAA-S-8081-14A, pg. 1-14.
Airplane Flying Handbook FAA--H-8083-3, pg. 5-8 $\Rightarrow$ 5-10.
Pilot Operating Handbook/Approved Flight Manual

SHORT-FIELD TAKEOFF AND MAXIMUM PERFORMANCE CLIMB

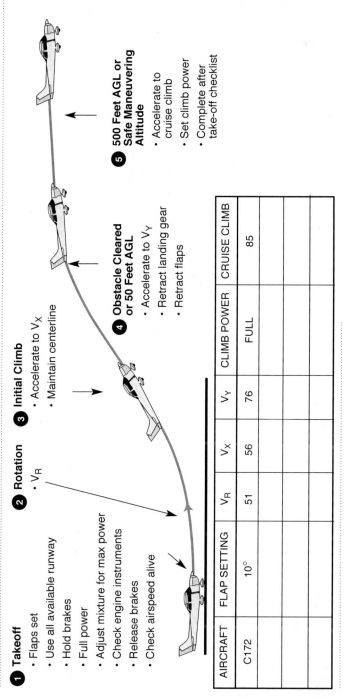

1 Takeoff
- Flaps set
- Use all available runway
- Hold brakes
- Full power
- Adjust mixture for max power
- Check engine instruments
- Release brakes
- Check airspeed alive

2 Rotation
- V_R

3 Initial Climb
- Accelerate to V_X
- Maintain centerline

4 Obstacle Cleared or 50 Feet AGL
- Accelerate to V_Y
- Retract landing gear
- Retract flaps

5 500 Feet AGL or Safe Maneuvering Altitude
- Accelerate to cruise climb
- Set climb power
- Complete after take-off checklist

AIRCRAFT	FLAP SETTING	V_R	V_X	V_Y	CLIMB POWER	CRUISE CLIMB
C172	10°	51	56	76	FULL	85

Limitations — V_X +10/-5 Knots • V_Y +10/-5 Knots

SOFT-FIELD TAKEOFF AND CLIMB

OBJECTIVE

To teach the private student the knowledge of the elements related to a soft-field takeoff and climb.

COMPLETION STANDARDS

1. Positions the flight controls for the existing wind conditions and to maximize lift as quickly as possible.
2. Clears the area; taxies onto the takeoff surface at a speed consistent with safety and aligns the airplane without stopping while advancing the throttle smoothly to takeoff power.
3. Establishes and maintains the pitch attitude that will transfer the weight of the airplane from the wheels to the wings as rapidly as possible.
4. Lifts off at the lowest possible airspeed and remains in ground effect while accelerating to V_X or V_Y as appropriate.
5. Establishes the pitch attitude for V_X or V_Y, as appropriate, and maintains selected airspeed +10/-5 knots, during the climb.
6. Retracts the landing gear, if appropriate, and flaps after clear of any obstacles or as recommended by the manufacturer.
7. Maintains takeoff power and V_X or V_Y +10/-5 knots to a safe maneuvering altitude.
8. Maintains directional control and proper wind-drift correction throughout the takeoff and climb.
9. Completes the appropriate checklist.

DESCRIPTION

A nose high attitude is maintained during the takeoff roll so as to transfer the airplane's weight to its wings and lift off as soon as possible. After lift off, the airplane is flown in ground effect until it accelerates to a safe flying speed.

PROCEDURE

1. Set wing flaps to recommended setting.
2. Adjust the mixture control if stated conditions warrant.
3. Take note of obstructions or hazards, if so stated.
4. Clear final approach.

5. Obtain clearance from the tower or announce intentions on the common traffic advisory frequency.

6. Taxi onto the takeoff surface, at a speed consistent with safety, with the yoke in the full aft position and ailerons in the correct position for existing wind conditions.

7. Align the airplane on the takeoff path without stopping, advance the throttle positively and smoothly to maximum allowable power, and check the engine instruments.

8. After the nose wheel lifts off, relax back pressure to maintain nose wheel clearance off the runway. Exercise caution to avoid over-rotating.

9. Maintain directional control on runway centerline by use of the rudder. Avoid using the brakes. (The stall warning horn may sound.)

10. Lift off as soon as possible, lower the pitch as necessary to remain in ground effect while accelerating.

11. As the airspeed approaches V_X with an obstacle or V_Y without an obstacle, establish and maintain V_X or V_Y pitch attitude.

12 Maintain V_X until the obstacle is cleared in necessary.

13. Retract the wing flaps when at a safe altitude (minimum 50 feet AGL) and at safe speed.

14. Maintain V_Y.

15. Retract landing gear after positive rate of climb and a safe landing can no longer be accomplished on the remaining runway. Also allow the gear to be air dried before raising it if taking off in wet snow or slush.

16. Maintain takeoff power and V_Y to 500 feet AGL or until all obstacles are cleared.

17. Accelerate to cruise climb airspeed then set climb power.

18. Maintain a straight track over the extended runway centerline until a turn is required.

19. Avoid noise sensitive areas.

20. Complete after-takeoff checklist.

Note: FAR 91.103 requires takeoff and landing performance data to be computed prior to all flights.

References
Private Pilot Practical Test Standards FAA-S-8081-14A, pg. 1-12.
Airplane Flying Handbook FAA-H-8083-3, pg. 5-10, 5-11.
Pilot Operating Handbook/Approved Flight Manual

SOFT-FIELD TAKEOFF AND CLIMB

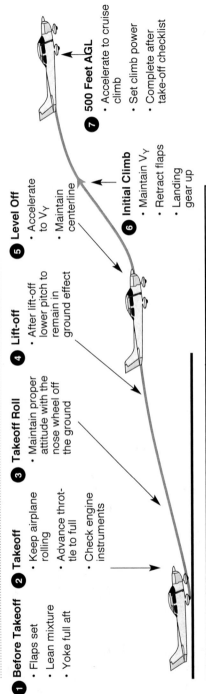

1 Before Takeoff
- Flaps set
- Lean mixture
- Yoke full aft

2 Takeoff
- Keep airplane rolling
- Advance throttle to full
- Check engine instruments

3 Takeoff Roll
- Maintain proper attitude with the nose wheel off the ground

4 Lift-off
- After lift-off lower pitch to remain in ground effect

5 Level Off
- Accelerate to V_Y
- Maintain centerline

6 Initial Climb
- Maintain V_Y
- Retract flaps
- Landing gear up

7 500 Feet AGL
- Accelerate to cruise climb
- Set climb power
- Complete after take-off checklist

AIRCRAFT	FLAP SETTING	V_R	V_X	V_Y	CLIMB POWER	CRUISE CLIMB
C172	10°	51	56	76	FULL	85

Limitations — V_Y +10/-5 Knots

TRAFFIC PATTERN OPERATIONS

OBJECTIVE

To teach the private student the knowledge of the elements related to traffic patterns. This shall include procedures at airports with and without operating control towers, prevention of runway incursions, collision avoidance, wake turbulence avoidance, and wind shear.

COMPLETION STANDARDS

1. Complies with proper traffic pattern procedures.
2. Maintains proper spacing from other aircraft.
3. Corrects for wind drift to maintain the proper ground track.
4. Maintains orientation with the runway/landing area in use.
5. Maintains the traffic pattern altitude, ±100 feet (30 meters), and the appropriate airspeed, ±10 knots.

DESCRIPTION

This maneuver establishes standard procedures for departures, arrivals and traffic performing landing practice around controlled and uncontrolled airports.

ARRIVAL PROCEDURE

1. Determine the active runway and traffic pattern direction. Standard patterns are left turns.
2. Establish communications, announce intentions at appropriate distance or time.
3. Maintain strict vigilance for other aircraft established in the area.
4. Establish the airplane on a 45° ground track toward the midpoint of the downwind leg unless otherwise directed by the tower. Pattern altitude and airspeed should be established not less than two miles out. Standard pattern altitude is 1000 feet above field elevation. Maximum speed 200 knots.
5. Turn the airplane onto the downwind leg approximately one-half mile to one mile out from the active runway compensating for wind drift.
6. Maintain pattern altitude normal cruise airspeed unless traffic separation dictates otherwise.

7. Lower landing gear if retractable and complete the pre-landing checklist or GUMPS.
    a. Gas.
    b. Undercarriage.
    c. Mixture.
    d. Propellers.
    e. Seatbelts and Switches.

8. Opposite the point of intended landing, carb heat on, reduce power and maintain altitude.

9. Add 10° of flaps, or first setting, and establish downwind approach speed. (Use flaps and speed recommended by Pilots Operating Handbook/Approved Flight Manual POH/AFM or 1.5 V_{S0}).

10. Commence a turn to the base leg when at a 45° angle from the touch down point. This turn may have to be adjusted due to other traffic, ATC request, or winds.

11. Evaluate base key position. If high, fast or on proper approach path, adjust flaps as necessary (normally 20°, or second setting). If low or slow, delay on any increase in flaps until re-established on proper approach path. Coordinate pitch and power to maintain the desired approach angle and base approach speed. (Use flaps and speed recommended by the POH/AFM, or 1.4 V_{S0}).

12. Visually clear the final approach, opposite base leg, and commence your turn to final so as to roll out with the airplane aligned with the landing runway.

13. Continue to evaluate glide path. If high, fast or on proper approach path, adjust flaps as necessary (normally full). If low or slow, delay on any increase in flaps until re-established on proper approach path. Coordinate the pitch and power to maintain the desired approach angle and the final approach speed. (Use speed recommended by the POH/AFM, or 1.3 V_{S0}).

14. Execute appropriate landing procedures.

DEPARTURE PROCEDURE

1. After lift off, maintain proper runway alignment and appropriate climb airspeeds.

2. If departing the traffic pattern, upon reaching a safe altitude, clear of obstacles but not less than 500 feet AGL, accelerate to cruise climb airspeed. (Use speed recommended by the POH/AFM or 10 knots above V_Y).

3. Upon reaching the traffic pattern altitude and beyond the departure end of the runway depart on a 45° ground track in the direction of traffic pattern, or proceed straight out.

4. Continue climb and conduct shallow clearing turns of 10° to 15° to cruise altitude.

5. For closed pattern operation, begin the turn to crosswind leg within 300 feet of traffic pattern altitude.

6. Once established at pattern or cruise altitude, whichever applies, pitch to level flight attitude, allow airspeed to increase to the desired airspeed, set power to desired, and trim.

Note: The above procedures assume an ideal pattern situation. Additional traffic, ATC, wind, local pattern restrictions, obstacles, etc., may dictate modification of these procedures. In all cases, the pilot shall exercise good judgement, situational awareness and maintain positive airplane control.

References
Private Pilot Practical Test Standards FAA-S-8081-14A, pg. 1-9.
Airplane Flying Handbook FAA-H-8083-3, pg. 7-1 ⇒ 7-4, 8-1 ⇒ 8-5.
Pilot's Handbook of Aeronautical Knowledge AC 61-23/FAA-H-8083-25, pg. 12-1 ⇒ 12-9.
Recommended Standard Traffic Patterns and Practices for Aeronautical Operations At Airports Without Operating Control Towers AC 90-66.
Aeronautical Information Manual, para. 4-1-1 ⇒ 4-1-13, 4-3-1 ⇒ 4-3-5.
Federal Aviation Regulation 91.117.

TRAFFIC PATTERN OPERATIONS — 1

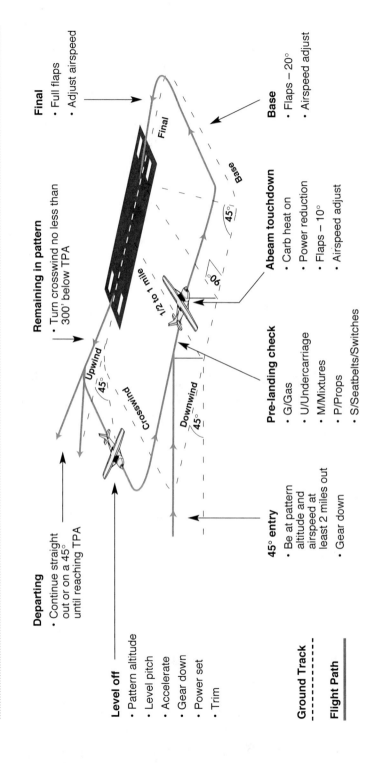

Departing
- Continue straight out or on a 45° until reaching TPA

Final
- Full flaps
- Adjust airspeed

Remaining in pattern
- Turn crosswind no less than 300' below TPA

Base
- Flaps – 20°
- Airspeed adjust

Abeam touchdown
- Carb heat on
- Power reduction
- Flaps – 10°
- Airspeed adjust

Pre-landing check
- G/Gas
- U/Undercarriage
- M/Mixtures
- P/Props
- S/Seatbelts/Switches

45° entry
- Be at pattern altitude and airspeed at least 2 miles out
- Gear down

Level off
- Pattern altitude
- Level pitch
- Accelerate
- Gear down
- Power set
- Trim

Final

Base

90°

45°

45°

Upwind

Crosswind

Downwind

45°

1/2 to 1 mile

Ground Track ———

Flight Path - - - - -

TRAFFIC PATTERN OPERATIONS — 2

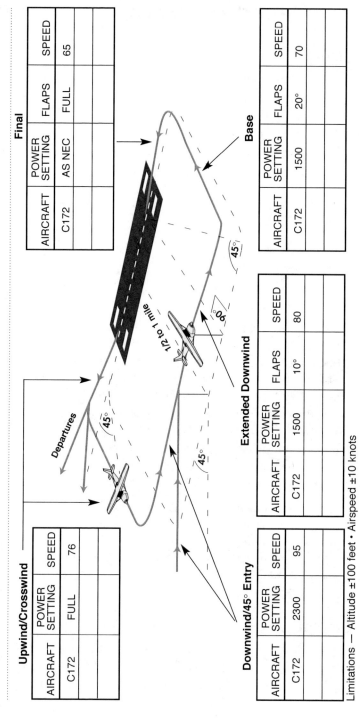

Upwind/Crosswind

AIRCRAFT	POWER SETTING	SPEED
C172	FULL	76

Final

AIRCRAFT	POWER SETTING	FLAPS	SPEED
C172	AS NEC	FULL	65

Base

AIRCRAFT	POWER SETTING	FLAPS	SPEED
C172	1500	20°	70

Extended Downwind

AIRCRAFT	POWER SETTING	FLAPS	SPEED
C172	1500	10°	80

Downwind/45° Entry

AIRCRAFT	POWER SETTING	SPEED
C172	2300	95

Limitations — Altitude ±100 feet • Airspeed ±10 knots

NORMAL APPROACH AND LANDING

OBJECTIVE

To teach the private student the knowledge of the elements related to a normal approach and landing.

COMPLETION STANDARDS

1. Considers the wind conditions, landing surface, obstructions, and selects a suitable touchdown point.
2. Establishes the recommended approach and landing configuration and airspeed, and adjusts pitch attitude and power as required.
3. Maintains a stabilized approach and the recommended airspeed, or in its absence, not more than 1.3 V_{S0}, +10/-5 knots, with gust factor applied.
4. Makes smooth, timely, and correct control application during the roundout and touchdown.
5. Remains aware of the possibility of wind shear and/or wake turbulence.
6. Touches down at or within 400 feet (120 meters) beyond a specified point.with no drift, and with the airplane's longitudinal axis aligned with and over the runway center/landing path.
7. Maintains crosswind correction and directional control throughout the approach and landing sequence.
8. Completes the appropriate checklist.

DESCRIPTION

The airplane is aligned and stabilized on final approach with final flap setting. Pitch and power are coordinated to remain stabilized on the desired glide path. At an appropriate altitude a transition to the landing attitude is made to allow a power off touchdown on the main gear. After touchdown, the airplane will be slowed to normal taxi speed on the runway centerline.

PROCEDURE

1. Prior to 300 feet AGL on final approach, stabilize the airplane with the final flap settings and recommended airspeed.
2. With the airplane stabilized, trim off control pressures.

3. During gusty conditions increase final approach speed by one-half the gust factor. So, if the wind is gusting to 12 knots, add 6 knots to your final approach speed.

4. Coordinate pitch and power to maintain the glide path that permits touchdown near stalling speed beyond and within 400 feet of a specified point.

5. At the appropriate flare altitude (10 to 20 feet AGL), slow the airplane descent rate by raising the pitch attitude and gradually reducing power to idle. The airplane will then settle onto the runway on the main gear in the landing attitude.

6. Maintain back pressure on the yoke throughout the landing roll.

7. Slow the airplane to taxi speed before leaving the runway centerline.

Note: FAR 91.103 requires takeoff and landing performance data to be computed prior to all flights.

References
Private Pilot Practical Test Standards FAA-S-8081-14A, pg. 1-11.
Airplane Flying Handbook FAA-H-8083-3, pg. 8-1 ⇒ 8-17.

CROSSWIND APPROACH AND LANDING

OBJECTIVE

To teach the private student the knowledge of the elements related to a crosswind approach and landing.

COMPLETION STANDARDS

1. Considers the wind conditions, landing surface, obstructions, and selects a suitable touchdown point.

2. Establishes the recommended approach and landing configuration and airspeed, and adjusts pitch attitude and power as required.

3. Maintains a stabilized approach and the recommended airspeed, or in its absence, not more than 1.3 V_{S0}, +10/-5 knots, with gust factor applied.

4. Makes smooth, timely, and correct control application during the roundout and touchdown.

5. Remains aware of the possibility of wind shear and/or wake turbulence.

6. Touches down at or within 400 feet (120 meters) beyond a specified point.with no drift, and with the airplane's longitudinal axis aligned with and over the runway center/landing path.

7. Maintains crosswind correction and directional control throughout the approach and landing sequence.

8. Completes the appropriate checklist.

DESCRIPTION

The airplane is aligned on final approach with final flap setting as dictated by wind conditions. Pitch and power are coordinated to remain stabilized on the desired glide path. At a point prior to round out, a crosswind correction is established using the side-slip method. At an appropriate altitude, a round out is made to the landing attitude. A power off touchdown on the upwind main gear first occurs, followed by normal deceleration and slow application of full aileron into the wind.

PROCEDURE

1. Once established on final approach, maintain runway alignment by use of an appropriate crab angle or side slip and extend the flaps to the final setting. The degree of flap setting will be determined by the existing conditions.

2. Use a final approach airspeed as recommended by the manufacturer. During gusty conditions increase final approach speed by one-half the gust factor. So, if the wind is gusting to 12 knots, add 6 knots to your final approach speed.

3. At a point prior to round out, drift correction will be maintained by establishing a side slip (wing-low) method of drift correction. (Apply aileron to control drift and opposite rudder to keep the airplane's longitudinal axis aligned with and over the runway centerline.)

4. Proper technique will result in a touchdown at approximate stall speed on the upwind main wheel first, followed by the downwind main wheel, then finally the nose wheel. Aileron deflection into the wind is increased to full during the landing roll out to prevent drift while rudder is used to maintain directional control.

Note: FAR 91.103 requires takeoff and landing performance data to be computed prior to all flights.

References
Private Pilot Practical Test Standards FAA-S-8081-14A, pg. 1-11.
Airplane Flying Handbook FAA-H-8083-3, pg. 8-1 ⇒ 8-17.

NORMAL/CROSSWIND APPROACH AND LANDING

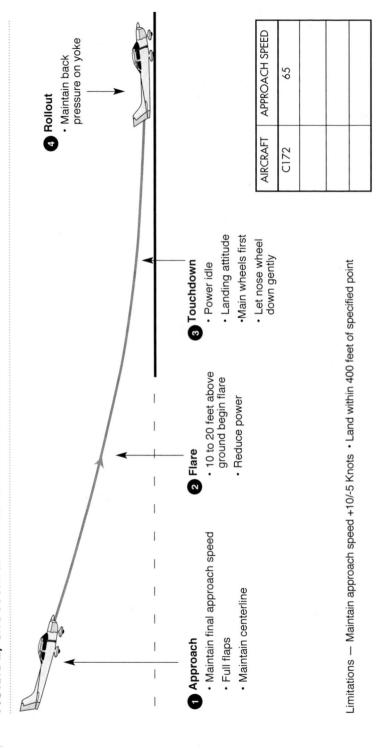

1 Approach
- Maintain final approach speed
- Full flaps
- Maintain centerline

2 Flare
- 10 to 20 feet above ground begin flare
- Reduce power

3 Touchdown
- Power idle
- Landing attitude
- Main wheels first
- Let nose wheel down gently

4 Rollout
- Maintain back pressure on yoke

AIRCRAFT	APPROACH SPEED
C172	65

Limitations — Maintain approach speed +10/-5 Knots • Land within 400 feet of specified point

SHORT-FIELD APPROACH AND LANDING

OBJECTIVE

To teach the private student the knowledge of the elements related to a short-field approach and landing.

COMPLETION STANDARDS

1. Considers the wind conditions, landing surface, obstructions, and selects the most suitable touchdown point.
2. Establishes the recommended approach and landing configuration and airspeed; adjusts pitch attitude and power as required.
3. Maintains a stabilized approach and recommended approach airspeed, or in its absence, not more than 1.3 V_{S0}, +10/-5 knots, with gust factor applied.
4. Makes smooth, timely, and correct control application during the roundout and touchdown.
5. Touches down smoothly at minimum control speed
6. Touches down at or within 200 feet (60 meters) beyond a specified point, with no side drift, minimum float, and with the airplane's longitudinal axis aligned with and over the runway center/landing path.
7. Maintains crosswind correction and directional control throughout the approach and landing.
8. Applies brakes, as necessary, to stop in the shortest distance consistent with safety.
9. Completes the appropriate checklist.

DESCRIPTION

A maximum performance maneuver requiring the use of procedures and techniques for approach and landing at fields with a relatively short landing lengths. Also, where an approach must be made over obstacles limiting the available landing length.

PROCEDURE

1. Set full flaps.
2. Coordinate pitch and power to obtain approach speed and the desired descent angle.

3. Ensure the approach is stabilized prior to 300 feet AGL.

4. Coordinate pitch and power to maintain the descent rate and airspeed.

5. Start the round out and power reductions so as to arrive at the power off stall attitude, near stall speed and with the throttle reaching idle at touchdown.

6. Lower the nose-wheel to the runway.

7. Retract the flaps.

8. Bring yoke full aft.

9. As weight is transferred from the wings to the main gear, increase braking to stop in the shortest distance consistent with safety.

Note: FAR 91.103 requires takeoff and landing performance data to be computed prior to all flights.

References
Private Pilot Practical Test Standards FAA-S-8081-14A, pg. 1-15.
Airplane Flying Handbook FAA- H-8083-3, pg. 8-17 ⇒ 8-19.
Pilot Operating Handbook/Approved Flight Manual

SHORT-FIELD APPROACH AND LANDING

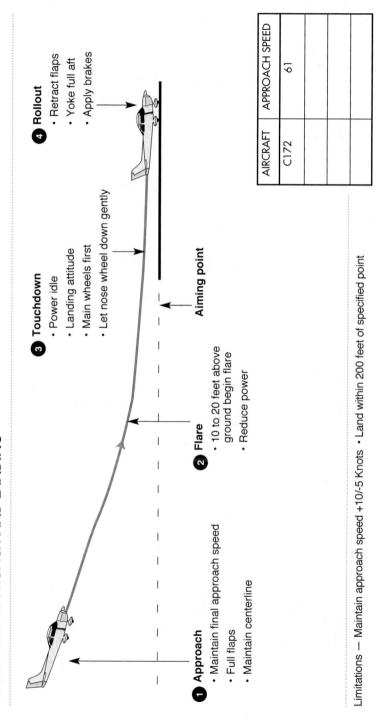

1 Approach
- Maintain final approach speed
- Full flaps
- Maintain centerline

2 Flare
- 10 to 20 feet above ground begin flare
- Reduce power

3 Touchdown
- Power idle
- Landing attitude
- Main wheels first
- Let nose wheel down gently

4 Rollout
- Retract flaps
- Yoke full aft
- Apply brakes

Aiming point

AIRCRAFT	APPROACH SPEED		
C172	61		

Limitations — Maintain approach speed +10/-5 Knots • Land within 200 feet of specified point

45

SOFT-FIELD APPROACH AND LANDING

OBJECTIVE

To teach the private student the knowledge of the elements related to a soft-field approach and landing.

COMPLETION STANDARDS

1. Considers the wind conditions, landing surface and obstructions, and selects the most suitable touchdown area.
2. Establishes the recommended approach and landing configuration and airspeed; adjusts pitch attitude and power as required.
3. Maintains a stabilized approach and recommended airspeed, or in its absence, not more than 1.3 V_{S0}, +10/-5 knots, with gust factor applied.
4. Makes smooth, timely, and correct control application during the roundout and touchdown.
5. Touches down softly with no drift, and with the airplane's longitudinal axis aligned with and the runway/landing path.
6. Maintains crosswind correction and directional control throughout the approach and landing sequence.
7. Maintains the correct position of the flight controls and sufficient speed to taxi on the soft surface.
8. Completes the appropriate checklist.

DESCRIPTION

When landing on rough or soft surfaces, the airplane must be controlled in such a manner that the wings support the weight of the airplane as long as practicable, to minimize drag and stresses imposed on the landing gear by the surface.

PROCEDURE

1. Set full flaps.
2. Coordinate pitch and power to obtain normal approach speed and descent angle.
3. Ensure the approach is stabilized prior to 300 feet AGL.

4. Commence round out at 20-30 feet, reducing power slightly so a residual power remains.

5. Slowly increase pitch as speed dissipates, leveling the airplane one to two feet above the surface.

6. Hold the airplane off as long as possible by increasing pitch to dissipate forward speed sufficiently. Adjust power as necessary touch down gently at minimum descent rate and speed.

7. Adjust power as necessary and continue to increase back pressure to keep the nose wheel off the ground.

8. When full aft yoke is reached, the nose will slowly drop. Slow the rate of drop by a slight addition of power.

Note: FAR 91.103 requires takeoff and landing performance data to be computed prior to all flights.

References
Private Pilot Practical Test Standards FAA-S-8081-14A, pg. 1-13.
Airplane Flying Handbook FAA-H-8083-3, pg. 8-19, 8-20.
Pilot Operating Handbook/Approved Flight Manual.

SOFT-FIELD APPROACH AND LANDING

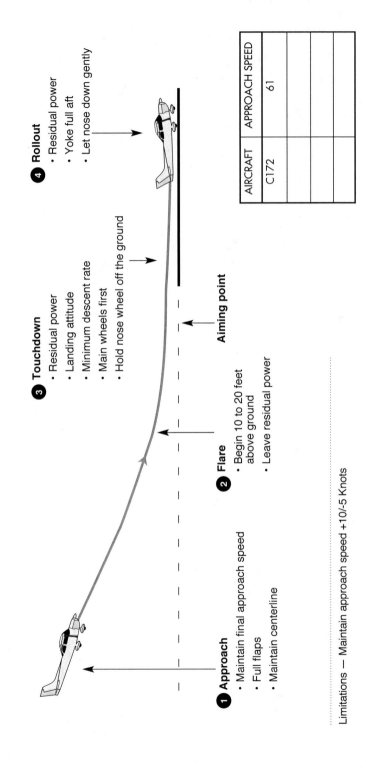

1 Approach
- Maintain final approach speed
- Full flaps
- Maintain centerline

2 Flare
- Begin 10 to 20 feet above ground
- Leave residual power

3 Touchdown
- Residual power
- Landing attitude
- Minimum descent rate
- Main wheels first
- Hold nose wheel off the ground

4 Rollout
- Residual power
- Yoke full aft
- Let nose down gently

Aiming point

AIRCRAFT	APPROACH SPEED		
C172	61		

Limitations — Maintain approach speed +10/-5 Knots

48

FORWARD SLIP TO LANDING

OBJECTIVE

To teach the private student the knowledge of the elements to a forward slip to a landing.

COMPLETION STANDARDS

1. Considers the wind conditions, landing surface and obstructions, and selects the most suitable touchdown point.
2. Establishes the slipping attitude at the point from which a landing can be made using the recommended approach and landing configuration and airspeed; adjusts pitch attitude and power as required.
3. Maintains a ground track aligned with the runway center/landing path and an airspeed which results in minimum float during the roundout.
4. Makes smooth, timely, and correct control application during the recovery from the slip, the roundout, and the touchdown.
5. Touches down smoothly at approximate stalling speed, at or within 400 feet (120 meters) beyond a specified point, with no side drift, and the airplane longitudinal axis aligned with the runway centerline.
6. Maintains crosswind correction and directional control throughout the approach and landing.
7. Completes the appropriate checklist.

DESCRIPTION

The forward slip is used to steepen the approach path without increasing airspeed, as would happen in a dive.

PROCEDURE

1. Note direction of wind.
2. Prior to 500 feet AGL on a slightly high final approach, stabilize the airplane with the recommended flap settings (usually zero and recommended normal approach airspeed).
3. Reduce power to idle.
4. Slip airplane into the wind by simultaneously adding aileron and full opposite rudder.

5. Adjust pitch to maintain desired airspeed. If slipping an airplane with one static port, there will be errors in the airspeed indicator. If the static port is located on the left side, then the airspeed will indicate lower than actual if slipping to the left. If slipping to the right then the airspeed will indicate higher than actual.

6. Use aileron control to maintain centerline.

7. At the appropriate time, recover from the slip by releasing the control inputs and raising the nose to the landing attitude.

8. Maintain back pressure on the yoke throughout the landing roll.

9. Slow the airplane to normal taxi speed before leaving the runway centerline.

Note: Consult the POH about limitations on slipping the airplane.

References
Private Pilot Practical Test Standards FAA-S-8081-14A, pg. 1-20.
Airplane Flying Handbook FAA-H-8083-3, pg. 8-10, 8-11.
Pilot Operating Handbook/Approved Flight Manual.

FORWARD SLIP TO LANDING

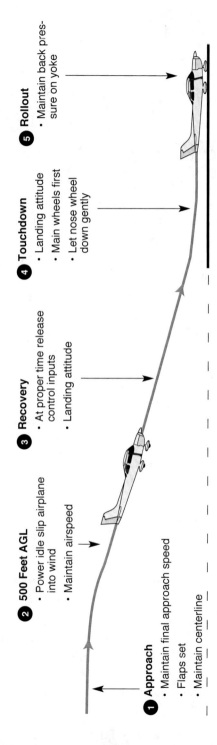

1 Approach
- Maintain final approach speed
- Flaps set
- Maintain centerline

2 500 Feet AGL
- Power idle slip airplane into wind
- Maintain airspeed

3 Recovery
- At proper time release control inputs
- Landing attitude

4 Touchdown
- Landing attitude
- Main wheels first
- Let nose wheel down gently

5 Rollout
- Maintain back pressure on yoke

AIRCRAFT	APPROACH SPEED	LEFT SLIP	RIGHT SLIP
C172	65	60	70

Limitations — Lands within 400 feet of specified point.

GO-AROUND/REJECTED LANDING

OBJECTIVE

To teach the private student the knowledge of the elements related to a go-around/rejected landing.

COMPLETION STANDARDS

1. Makes a timely decision to discontinue the approach to landing.
2. Applies takeoff power immediately and transitions to the climb pitch attitude for V_Y and maintains V_Y +10/-5 knots.
3. Retracts the flaps as appropriate.
4. Retracts the landing gear, if appropriate, after a positive rate of climb has been established.
5. Maneuvers to the side of the runway/landing area to clear and avoid conflicting traffic.
6. Maintains takeoff power V_Y +10/-5 knots to a safe maneuvering altitude.
7. Maintains directional control and proper wind-drift correction throughout the climb.
8. Completes the appropriate checklist.

DESCRIPTION

The landing approach is abandoned and the airplane is transitioned into the climb attitude and configuration.

PROCEDURE

1. Apply take-off power.
2. Carburetor heat cold.
3. Establish V_Y attitude as appropriate to attain V_Y airspeed.
4. Retract flaps in accordance with the POH.
5. As airspeed increases, retract the flaps on schedule as recommended in the POH.
6. Adjust pitch attitude for V_Y and when the safe flap retraction speed is reached, retract to flaps zero.
7. Retract landing gear, if retractable, after a positive rate of climb has been established.

8. If go-around was caused by another airplane, offset and pass to the right unless it will conflict with other traffic (a non-standard pattern), or tower directs otherwise.

9. Radio intentions.

References
Private Pilot Practical Test Standards FAA-S-8081-14A, pg. 1-20.
Airplane Flying Handbook FAA-H-8083-3, pg. 8-11 ⇒ 8-13.
Pilot Operating Handbook/Approved Flight Manual.

GO-AROUND/REJECTED LANDING

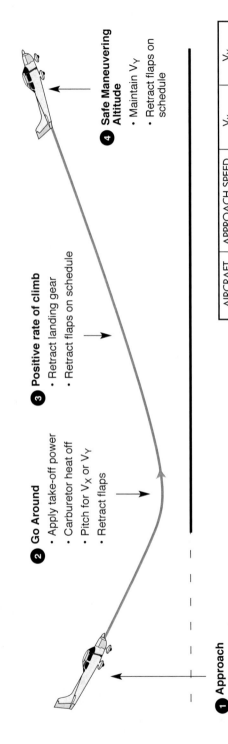

❷ Go Around
- Apply take-off power
- Carburetor heat off
- Pitch for V_X or V_Y
- Retract flaps

❸ Positive rate of climb
- Retract landing gear
- Retract flaps on schedule

❹ Safe Maneuvering Altitude
- Maintain V_Y
- Retract flaps on schedule

❶ Approach
- Maintain final approach speed
- Full flaps
- Maintain centerline

AIRCRAFT	APPROACH SPEED	V_X	V_Y
C172	65	56	76

Limitations — Maintains V_Y +10/-5 Knots

CHAPTER FOUR
PERFORMANCE MANEUVER

STEEP TURNS

OBJECTIVE

To teach the private student the knowledge of the elements related to steep turns.

COMPLETION STANDARDS

1. Establishes the manufacturer's recommended airspeed or if one is not stated, a safe airspeed not to exceed V_A.
2. Rolls into a coordinated 360° turn; maintains a 45° of bank.
3. Performs the task in the opposite direction, as specified by the examiner.
4. Divides attention between airplane control and orientation.
5. Maintains the entry altitude, ±100 feet (30 meters), airspeed, ±10 knots, bank, ±5°; and rolls out on the entry heading, ±10°.

DESCRIPTION

The "steep turn" maneuvers consists of a 360° turn in either direction, using a bank steep enough to cause an "over banking" tendency during which maximum turning performance is attained and relatively high load factors are imposed.

PROCEDURE

1. Clear the area.
2. Adjust the mixture for an anticipated increase in power.
3. Establish entry speed (below V_A) on specified heading and visual reference.
4. Smoothly roll into a coordinated turn in either direction using a bank angle of 45°.
5. As bank angle steepens, adjust back pressure so as to maintain a level attitude, adjust power to maintain airspeed and trim.
6. Increase power by 200 RPM/2" MP to maintain airspeed. Use throttle position, engine sound and control pressures to estimate the power setting. Avoid fixating on the RPM/MP gauge
7. Divide your attention between airplane control and orientation.
8. Maintain a constant bank angle, altitude and airspeed during the turn.

9. Plan to lead the roll out so the turn is stopped on specified heading.

10. Lead the roll-out by one-half the bank angle (22°) and roll-out at the same rate you rolled in.

11. Return to straight and level at cruise.

References

Private Pilot Practical Test Standards FAA-S-8081-14A, pg. 1-21.
Airplane Flying Handbook FAA-H-8083-3, pg. 9-1,9-2.
Pilot Operating Handbook/Approved Flight Manual.

AIRCRAFT	SPEED	POWER
C172	95	2300

Limitations — Altitude ±100 Feet • Airspeed ±10 Knots • Bank ±5°
Rolls Out On Entry Heading ±10°

CHAPTER FIVE
GROUND REFERENCE
MANEUVERS

RECTANGULAR COURSE

OBJECTIVE

To teach the private student the knowledge of the elements related to a rectangular course.

COMPLETION STANDARDS

1. Selects a suitable reference area.

2. Plans the maneuver so as to enter a left or right pattern, 600 to 1,000 feet AGL (180 to 300 meters) at an appropriate distance from the selected reference area, 45° to the downwind leg.

3. Applies adequate wind-drift correction during straight-and-turning flight to maintain a constant ground track around the rectangular reference area.

4. Divides attention between airplane control and the ground track while maintaining coordinated flight.

5. Maintains altitude, ±100 feet (30 meters); maintains airspeed, ±10 knots.

DESCRIPTION

A square or rectangular field is used as reference. Then a course is flown around that field with the ground track a constant distance from the field, while maintaining constant altitude and airspeed.

PROCEDURE

1. Clear the area.

2. Select a rectangular field with sides approximately one mile in length. Have an emergency landing spot within gliding distance available.

3. Enter the maneuver 45° to the downwind leg approximately 1/4 mile away from the field at 800 feet AGL.

4. When abeam a first corner of the field, begin a turn from downwind to base in the direction of the pattern. Use a bank angle necessary to maintain a constant radius turn. Normally the bank should not exceed 45°. The bank angle and the rate of roll will be steeper when turning from downwind to base due to the faster groundspeed. As the turn progresses, the bank angle will be reduced as the ground speed is reduced.

5. Roll out the airplane slightly towards the field to compensate for wind drift on the base leg.

6. When abeam the second corner corner of the field, begin a turn from base to upwind in the direction of the pattern. Use a bank angle necessary to maintain a constant radius turn. Normally the bank should not exceed 45°. The bank angle and the rate of roll will be shallower when turning from base to upwind due to the slower groundspeed. As the turn progresses, the bank angle will be reduced as the ground speed is reduced.

7. Roll out the airplane parallel to the field as you should not have to to compensate for wind drift on the upwind leg. However, if the wind is not blowing parallel to the field, apply crab to correct for wind-drift.

8. When abeam the third corner of the field, begin a turn from upwind to crosswind in the direction of the pattern. Use a bank angle necessary to maintain a constant radius turn. Normally the bank should not exceed 45°. The bank angle and the rate of roll will be shallower when turning from upwind to crosswind due to the slower groundspeed. As the turn progresses, the bank angle will be increased as the ground speed increases.

9. Roll out the airplane slightly away from the field to compensate for wind drift on the crosswind leg.

10. When abeam the last corner of the field, begin a turn from crosswind to downwind in the direction of the pattern. Use a bank angle necessary to maintain a constant radius turn. Normally the bank should not exceed 45°. The bank angle and the rate of roll will be steeper when turning from crosswind to downwind due to the faster groundspeed. As the turn progresses, the bank angle will be increased as the ground speed increases.

11. Roll out the airplane parallel to the field as you should not have to to compensate for wind drift on the downwind leg. However, if the wind is not blowing parallel to the field, apply crab to correct for wind-drift.

12. Divide attention between coordinated airplane control, ground track and collision avoidance.

13. Adjust power to maintain entry airspeed.

References
Private Pilot Practical Test Standards FAA-S-8081-14A, pg. 1-22.
Airplane Flying Handbook FAA-H-8083-3, pg. 6-4 ⇒ 6-6.

RECTANGULAR COURSE

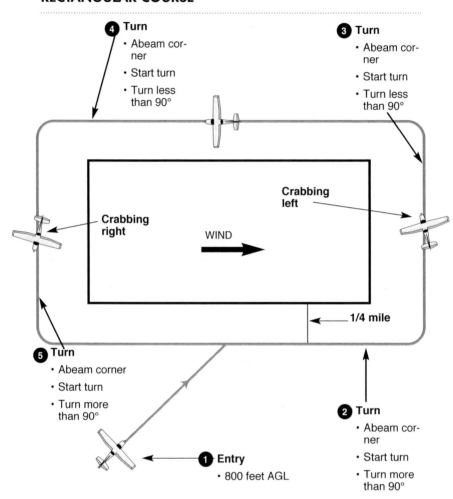

4 Turn
- Abeam corner
- Start turn
- Turn less than 90°

3 Turn
- Abeam corner
- Start turn
- Turn less than 90°

Crabbing left

Crabbing right

WIND

1/4 mile

5 Turn
- Abeam corner
- Start turn
- Turn more than 90°

2 Turn
- Abeam corner
- Start turn
- Turn more than 90°

1 Entry
- 800 feet AGL

AIRCRAFT	POWER SETTING	SPEED
C172	2300	95

Limitations — Altitude ±100 Feet • Airspeed ±10 Knots

S-TURNS ACROSS A ROAD

OBJECTIVE

To teach the private student the knowledge of the elements related to S-turns.

COMPLETION STANDARDS

1. Selects a suitable ground reference line.
2. Plans the maneuver so as to enter at 600 to 1000 feet (180 to 300 meters) AGL, perpendicular to the selected reference line,
3. Applies adequate wind-drift correction to track a constant radius turn on each side of the selected reference line.
4. Reverses the direction of the turn directly over the selected reference line.
5. Divides attention between airplane control and the ground track and maintains coordinated flight.
6. Maintains altitude. ±100 feet (30 meters); maintains airspeed, ±10 knots.

DESCRIPTION

A straight line on the ground is used as reference. A ground track of semicircles of equal radii on each side of the reference line, while maintaining constant altitude and airspeed.

PROCEDURE

1. Clear the area.
2. Select a straight line on the ground downwind from the airplane. Have an emergency landing spot within gliding distance available.
3. Enter the maneuver perpendicular to the reference line at 800 feet AGL.
4. When over the reference line, begin a turn to the left or right using the bank angle necessary to maintain a constant radius from the reference line. Normally the bank angle should not exceed 45°.
5. During the downwind portion of the turn, the bank angle will be steeper than upwind portion due to higher groundspeed.

6. Divide attention between coordinated airplane control, ground track, and collision avoidance.

7. Apply the necessary wind-drift corrections to maintain a constant radius turn on each side of the reference line. The bank angle should be constantly changing, either slowly increasing or decreasing.

8. Adjust power to maintain entry airspeed.

9. Transition the airplane such that wings level occurs over the reference line and begin a turn in opposite direction immediately.

References
Private Pilot Practical Test Standards FAA-S-8081-14A, pg. 1-22.
Airplane Flying Handbook FAA-8083-3, pg. 6-6, 6-7.

S-TURNS ACROSS A ROAD

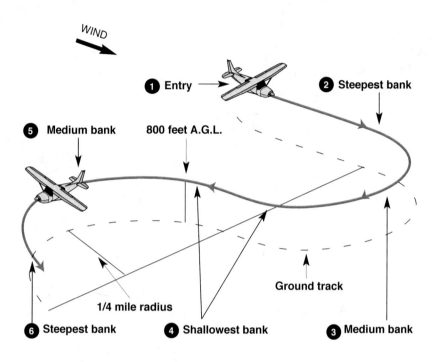

WIND

1 Entry

2 Steepest bank

5 Medium bank

800 feet A.G.L.

6 Steepest bank

4 Shallowest bank

3 Medium bank

Ground track

1/4 mile radius

AIRCRAFT	POWER SETTING	SPEED
C172	2300	95

Limitations — Altitude ±100 Feet • Airspeed ±10 Knots

TURNS AROUND A POINT

OBJECTIVE

To teach the private student the knowledge of the elements related to turns around a point.

COMPLETION STANDARDS

1. Selects a suitable round reference point.
2. Plans the maneuver so as to enter at 600 to 1000 feet (180 to 300 meters) AGL, at an appropriate distance from the reference point.
3. Applies adequate wind-drift correction to track a constant radius turn around the selected reference.
4. Divides attention between airplane control and the ground track and maintains coordinated flight.
5. Maintains altitude. ±100 feet (30 meters); maintains airspeed, ±10 knots.

DESCRIPTION

A point selected on the ground is used as reference. At least two turns are made around that point, with the ground track at a constant radius from the point, while maintaining constant altitude and airspeed.

PROCEDURE

1. Clear the area.
2. Select a point downwind from the airplane. Have an emergency landing spot within gliding distance available.
3. Set power for desired airspeed and trim.
4. Enter the maneuver on the upwind side perpendicular to the point at 800 feet AGL and 1/4 n.m. away.
5. When abeam the point, begin a turn in the direction of the point using the bank angle necessary to maintain a constant radius. The bank angle should be 45° at the steepest point in the turn. During the upwind portion of the turn, the bank angle will be shallower than a downwind portion due to slower groundspeed.
6. During the crosswind portion of the turn, the airplane will be crabbed into the wind.

7. Divide attention between coordinated airplane control, ground track, and collision avoidance.

8. Adjust power as necessary to maintain entry airspeed and trim.

References

Private Pilot Practical Test Standards FAA-S-8081-14A, pg. 1-23.
Airplane Flying Handbook FAA-H-8083-3, pg. 6-7 ⇒ 6-9.

TURNS AROUND A POINT

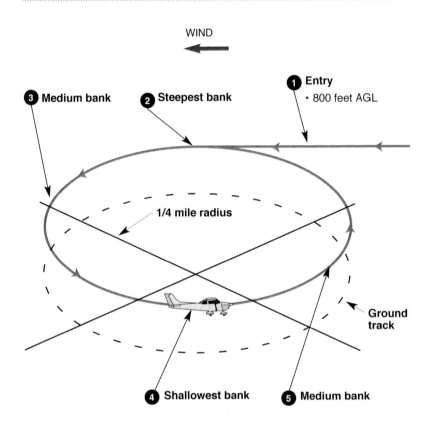

WIND

3 Medium bank **2** Steepest bank **1** Entry
• 800 feet AGL

1/4 mile radius

Ground track

4 Shallowest bank **5** Medium bank

AIRCRAFT	POWER SETTING	SPEED
C172	2300	95

Limitations — Altitude ±100 Feet • Airspeed ±10 Knots

CHAPTER SIX

NAVIGATION

NAVIGATION SYSTEMS AND RADAR SERVICES

OBJECTIVE

To teach the private pilot student the knowledge of the elements related to navigation systems and radar services.

COMPLETION STANDARDS

1. Demonstrates the ability to use an airborne electronic navigation system.
2. Locates the airplane's position using the navigation system.
3. Intercepts and tracks a given course, radial or bearing, as appropriate.
4. Recognizes and describes the indication of station passage, if appropriate.
5. Recognizes signal loss and takes appropriate action.
6. Uses communication procedures when utilizing radar services.
7. Maintains the appropriate altitude, ±200 feet (60 meters) and headings ±15°.

DESCRIPTION

The aircraft is maneuvered so as to intercept and track a predetermined navigational radial or bearing.

PROCEDURE

1. Intercepting a VOR, GPS or LORAN Radial

a. Tune and identify the station.
b. Reset the heading indicator by reference to the magnetic compass.
c. Turn the airplane to a heading parallel to the desired course. (Once you understand and can visualize this step, it may be skipped in order to expedite the entire procedure.)
d. Center the Course Deviation Indicator (CDI) with a "TO" flag if moving toward the station, and a "FROM" flag if moving away from the station. Now note the top indication of the Omni Bearing Selector (OBS). This is your present course.
e. Set the OBS to the desired course.

f. Double the difference between the present course and desired course to determine the intercept angle. This angle should not be less than 20° (may never get there) or greater than 90° (going the wrong way).

g. Turn the airplane the shortest distance toward the intercept heading and maintain that heading until the CDI starts to center.

h. As the CDI centers, turn on course and begin tracking procedures to correct for wind.

2. Tracking a VOR, GPS or LORAN Radial

a. When the desired course has been intercepted, with the CDI centered, maintain a heading which corresponds to the OBS setting.

b. Attempt to anticipate the affects of winds (winds aloft forecast) and place an appropriate wind correction angle.

c. When a definite off course indication is shown by the CDI, turn 20° toward the direction of the CDI needle.

d. Maintain the new heading until the CDI begins to recenter.

e. As the CDI recenters, turn 10° back toward the selected course. This establishes a wind correction angle of 10°. If the CDI remains centered, maintain the heading. The wind correction angle is correct.

f. If the CDI begins to show deflection in the direction opposite of the initial deviation, the 10° wind correction angle was too great. In this case, turn to a heading paralleling the course and allow the airplane to drift back onto the desired radial. When the CDI recenters, establish a 5° wind correction angle. Five degree corrections are normally adequate to keep the CDI centered after the approximate heading is established.

g. Ultimate accuracy will require corrections of less than 5°.

Note: If the first 20° of heading change fails to change the direction of the CDI movement within a reasonable period of time, another 20° heading change should be made toward the direction of CDI deflection to accumulate a wind correction angle of 40° (a strong crosswind is indicated). As the CDI recenters, establish a 20° correction angle. Adjust this angle as necessary, using the bracketing technique described above.

PROCEDURE

1. Intercepting a NDB Bearing

a. Tune and identify the station.

b. Set a volume level which allows constant monitoring of the NDB facility. There is no warning flag in the ADF system, so the only way to tell if we lose the station signal is loss of the audible signal.

c. Reset the heading indicator by reference to the magnetic compass.

d. Turn the airplane to a heading parallel to the desired bearing/course. (Once you understand and can visualize this procedure, this step may be skipped in order to expedite the entire procedure.)

e. Note the number of degrees between the top of the ADF azimuth or desired course, (180° point if intercepting a bearing from the station) and the ADF pointer, or present bearing/course.

f. Double this difference to determine the intercept angle. This angle should not be less than 20° (may never get there) or greater than 90° (going the wrong way).

g. Turn the airplane in the direction of the pointer to the intercept heading. Maintain that heading just prior to intercepting the desired bearing/course. The bearing/course will have been intercepted when the angle between the ADF pointer and the "nose" or "tail" is equal to the intercept angle.

h. Lead the pointer as required to roll out on the magnetic bearing/course with a relative bearing of 0° or 180° as appropriate.

2. Tracking a NDB Bearing

a. When the desired bearing/course has been intercepted, with the ADF pointer centered on the "nose" or "tail," maintain a heading corresponding to the bearing to be flown.

b. Attempt to anticipate the affects of winds (winds aloft forecast) and place an appropriate wind correction angle.

c. When a definite off-bearing/course deviation is indicated by a 5° pointer deflection, turn the airplane 20° toward the direction of the pointer deflection.

d. Maintain the new heading until the correction angle is equal to the angle between the ADF pointer and the "nose" or "tail."

e. Turn 10° back toward the original heading. This establishes a 10° wind correction angle.

f. If the ADF pointer deviates toward the "nose" (or further away from the "tail"), the 10° wind correction angle is insufficient. Turn another 10° in the direction of needle deflection, and after re-intercepting the bearing/course, establish a 15° wind correction angle. On the other hand, if the ADF pointer deviates further away from the "nose" (or towards the "tail"), the 10° wind correction angle is too great. In this case, turn parallel to the bearing/course and allow the airplane to drift back on bearing. Once established on-bearing/course, establish a 5° correction angle. Note: If the first 20° of heading change does not provide sufficient correction angle to reestablish the course within a reasonable period of time, another 20° heading change should be made in the direction of pointer deflection to accumulate a wind correction angle of 40° (a strong crosswind is indicated). When the ADF pointer is at a 40° angle to the 0° "nose" or 180° "tail" position, establish a 20° wind correction angle. Adjust this angle as necessary using the bracketing technique described above.

References

Private Pilot Practical Test Standards FAA-S-8081-14A, pg. 1-24.
Airplane Flying Handbook FAA-H-8083-3.
Pilot's Handbook of Aeronautical Knowledge AC 61-23/FAA-H-8083-25 pg. 14-17 ⇒ 14-27.
Aeronautical Information Manual, para. 1-1-2 ⇒ 1-2-4.
Navigation Equipment Operations Manual.
Instrument Flying Handbook FAA-H-8083-15, pg. 7-3 ⇒ 7-27.

INTERCEPTING AND TRACKING VOR/GPS/LORAN RADIALS

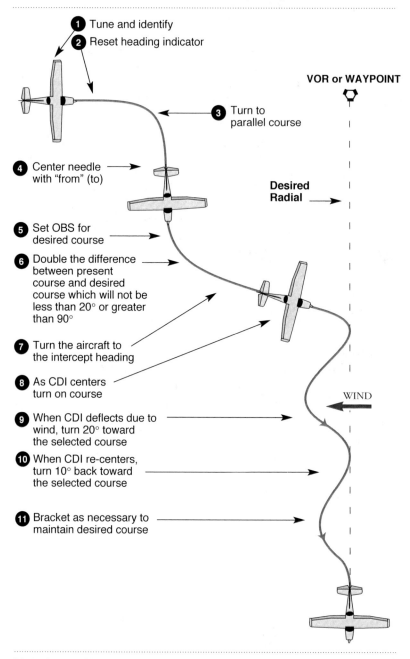

1 Tune and identify

2 Reset heading indicator

VOR or WAYPOINT

3 Turn to parallel course

4 Center needle with "from" (to)

Desired Radial

5 Set OBS for desired course

6 Double the difference between present course and desired course which will not be less than 20° or greater than 90°

7 Turn the aircraft to the intercept heading

8 As CDI centers turn on course

WIND

9 When CDI deflects due to wind, turn 20° toward the selected course

10 When CDI re-centers, turn 10° back toward the selected course

11 Bracket as necessary to maintain desired course

Limitations — Altitude ± 200 Feet • Headings ±15°

INTERCEPTING AND TRACKING NDB BEARINGS

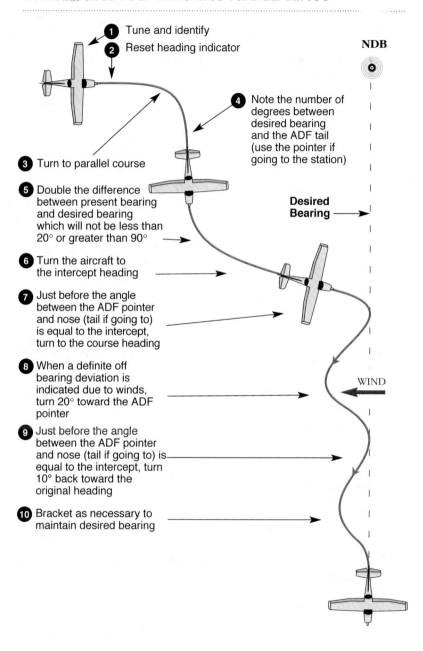

1 Tune and identify

2 Reset heading indicator

NDB

4 Note the number of degrees between desired bearing and the ADF tail (use the pointer if going to the station)

3 Turn to parallel course

Desired Bearing ——→

5 Double the difference between present bearing and desired bearing which will not be less than 20° or greater than 90°

6 Turn the aircraft to the intercept heading

7 Just before the angle between the ADF pointer and nose (tail if going to) is equal to the intercept, turn to the course heading

8 When a definite off bearing deviation is indicated due to winds, turn 20° toward the ADF pointer

WIND

9 Just before the angle between the ADF pointer and nose (tail if going to) is equal to the intercept, turn 10° back toward the original heading

10 Bracket as necessary to maintain desired bearing

Limitations — Altitude ± 200 Feet • Headings ±15°

DIVERSION

OBJECTIVE

To teach the private student the knowledge and skill of the elements related to diversion.

COMPLETION STANDARDS

1. Selects an appropriate alternate airport and route.
2. Makes an accurate estimate of heading, groundspeed, arrival time, and fuel consumption to the alternate airport.
3. Maintains the appropriate altitude, ±200 feet (60 meters) and established heading, ±15°.

DESCRIPTION

The airplane is diverted from its original course to an alternate airport when continuation of the flight is impractical due to weather, fuel, aeromedical factors, equipment failure, etc.

PROCEDURE

1. Select alternate airport on the sectional chart, considering airport services.
2. Determine present location by use of navigational facilities, prominent landmarks and/or time from last known location.
3. Determine the magnetic course from a point where you estimate turning (usually one to two miles ahead) to the alternate.
   a. Using a straight edge, such as a pen or pencil, align it with the new course between your estimated turn point and the alternate airport.
   b. Maintain the straight edge in the same relative position and slide it to the nearest compass rose of a VOR.
   c. Estimate the new magnetic course.
4. Using the forecasted winds aloft, adjust the estimated magnetic course to determine the new magnetic heading to the alternate airport.
5. Reset the heading indicator with reference to the magnetic compass.
6. Turn the airplane in the shortest direction to the new heading.

7. Note time on sectional or paper.

8. Measure the distance of your new course.

9. Using your true airspeed and the forecasted winds aloft, guesstimate the approximate ground speed.

10. Compute the estimated time enroute (ETE).

11. Compute the required fuel burn for the diversion using the GPH or PPH for that altitude and ensure there is adequate fuel for the diversion plus required reserves.

12. Change altitude if necessary to comply with FAR 91.159 "VFR cruising altitude."

13. Contact the nearest FSS and inform them of your diversion from your originally filed flight plan.

14. Use all three types of navigation to find the alternate airport.
    a. Pilotage.
    b. Dead reckoning.
    c. Radio navigation.

Note: Refer to the appendix for a checklist.

References
Private Pilot Practical Test Standards FAA-S-8081-14A, pg. 1-25.
Pilots Handbook of Aeronautical Knowledge AC 61-23/FAA-H-8083-25, pg. 14-27.
Aeronautical Information Manual.

LOST PROCEDURES

OBJECTIVE

To teach the private student the knowledge of the elements related to lost procedures.

COMPLETION STANDARDS

1. Selects an appropriate course of action.
2. Maintains an appropriate heading and climbs, if necessary.
3. Identifies prominent landmarks.
4. Uses navigation systems/facilities and/or contacts an ATC facility for assistance, as appropriate.

DESCRIPTION

Procedures to help a pilot who becomes disoriented and loses track of his/her position during a flight.

PROCEDURE

1. Continue flying original or appropriate heading.
2. Recheck flight plan calculations for accuracy.
3. Remember the **FIVE C'S**.
4. **Climb** to a higher altitude, if weather permits, so visual references are more visible, radio navigation is easier to receive, to increase communication range, and have better radar and direction finding detection.
   a. Proceed to the nearest concentration of prominent landmarks and attempt to locate them on your sectional.
   b. Attempt to determine position using the VOR and/or ADF and DME if equipped.
5. **Circle** in a shallow bank.
6. **Confess.** If you are unable to determine your location by this point, you need assistance.
7. **Communicate** with the appropriate facility for assistance.
   a. Air Route Traffic Control Center.
   b. Flight Service Station.
   c. Tower.
   d. Emergency frequency 121.5 MHz.

8. **Comply** with what the facility tells you to do.

References

Private Pilot Practical Test Standards FAA-S-8081-14A, pg. 1-25
Pilot's Handbook of Aeronautical Knowledge AC 61-23/FAA-H-8083-25,
pg. 4-27.
Aeronautical Information Manual, para. 6-2-1 $\Rightarrow$ 6-2-3.

CHAPTER SEVEN
SLOW FLIGHT AND STALLS

MANEUVERING DURING SLOW FLIGHT

OBJECTIVE

To teach the private student the knowledge of the elements related to maneuvering during slow flight.

COMPLETION STANDARDS

1. Selects an entry altitude that will allow the task to be completed no lower than 1,500 feet (460 meters) AGL.
2. Establishes and maintains an airspeed at which further increase in angle of attack, increase in load factor, or reduction of power, would result in an immediate stall.
3. Accomplishes coordinated straight-and-level flight, turns, climbs, and descents with landing gear and flap configurations specified by the examiner.
4. Divides attention between airplane control and orientation.
5. Maintains the specified altitude, ±100 feet (30 meters); specified heading, ±10°; airspeed, +10/-0 knots; and specified angle of bank, ±10°.

DESCRIPTION

A slow airspeed is established and maintained while performing turns, climbs, and descents.

PROCEDURE

1. Clear the area.
2. After completing the clearing turns, apply the carburetor heat, adjust the mixture for the anticipation of full power and reduce power to 1,500 rpm.
3. Maintain heading and altitude while slowing to 1.2 V_{S1}.
4. Extend flaps to specified setting when the airspeed enters the flap operating range.
5. Lower landing gear if specified.
6. As airspeed approaches desired airspeed, increase power to maintain altitude and turn carburetor heat off. Further adjust power as required.

7. Turns, climbs and descents using various configurations are performed as directed by the instructor/examiner while maintaining the desired airspeed.

8. Recovery initiated by applying full power and adjusting pitch attitude to maintain altitude while retracting flaps and landing gear.

9. Resume normal cruise, or as directed.

References
Private Pilot Practical Test Standards FAA-S-8081-14A, pg. 1-26.
Airplane Flying Handbook FAA-H-8083-3, pg. 4-1, 4-2.
Pilot Operating Handbook/Approved Flight Manual.

MANEUVERING DURING SLOW FLIGHT

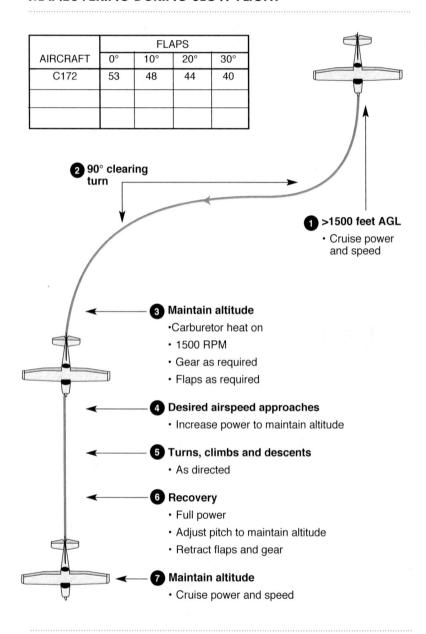

AIRCRAFT	FLAPS			
	0°	10°	20°	30°
C172	53	48	44	40

2 **90° clearing turn**

1 **>1500 feet AGL**
- Cruise power and speed

3 **Maintain altitude**
- Carburetor heat on
- 1500 RPM
- Gear as required
- Flaps as required

4 **Desired airspeed approaches**
- Increase power to maintain altitude

5 **Turns, climbs and descents**
- As directed

6 **Recovery**
- Full power
- Adjust pitch to maintain altitude
- Retract flaps and gear

7 **Maintain altitude**
- Cruise power and speed

Limitations — Maintains at least 1,500 Feet AGL • Maintains specific heading ±10° • Maintains bank angle ±10° • Maintains altitude ±100 Feet (30 Meters) • Maintains airspeed +10/-0 Knots

POWER-OFF STALLS

OBJECTIVE

To teach the private student the knowledge of the elements related to power-off stalls.

COMPLETION STANDARDS

1. Selects an entry altitude that will allow the task to be completed no lower than 1,500 feet (460 meters) AGL.
2. Establishes a stabilized approach in the approach or landing configuration, as specified by the examiner.
3. Transitions smoothly from the approach or landing attitude to a pitch attitude that will induce a stall.
4. Maintains a specified heading, ±10°, if in straight flight; maintains a specified angle of bank not to exceed 20°, ±10°, if in turning flight, while inducing the stall.
5. Recognizes and recovers promptly after the stall occurs by simultaneously reducing the angle of attack, increasing power to maximum allowable, and leveling the wings to return to a straight-and-level flight attitude with a minimum loss of altitude appropriate for the airplane.
6. Retracts the flaps to the recommended setting; retracts the landing gear, if retractable, after a positive rate of climb is established;
7. Accelerates to V_X or V_Y before the final flap retraction; returns to the altitude, heading, and airspeed specified by the examiner.

DESCRIPTION

The airplane is stabilized during entry at the airspeed, configuration, and power setting appropriate for landing approach. The pitch attitude is then raised that will induce a full stall. A recovery is initiated promptly after the full stall.

PROCEDURE

1. Clear the area.
2. After completing the clearing turns, apply carburetor heat and reduce power to 1,500 RPM.
3. Maintain heading and altitude while slowing to approach speed.

4. Once airspeed is in the flap operating range, lower flaps and landing gear to the landing setting (or as directed).

5. Reduce power to idle and establish glide at final approach speed.

6. For turning stalls, establish a 20° bank in either direction.

7. Continue increasing the pitch attitude, announcing any buffeting, until a full stall occurs.

8. Initiate recovery by lowering nose and simultaneously applying full power while using coordinated aileron and rudder to level the wings.

9. Carburetor heat off.

10. Adjust pitch to minimize altitude loss.

11. Retract flaps as recommended in the POH.

12. Once a positive recovery is assured, slowly raise flaps, landing gear and accelerate to cruise speed.

References

Private Pilot Practical Test Standards FAA-S-8081-14A, pg. 1-27.
Airplane Flying Handbook FAA-H-8083-3, pg. 4-3 4-8.
Stall and Spin Awareness Training AC 61-67.
Pilot Operating Handbook/Approved Flight Manual.

POWER-OFF STALLS

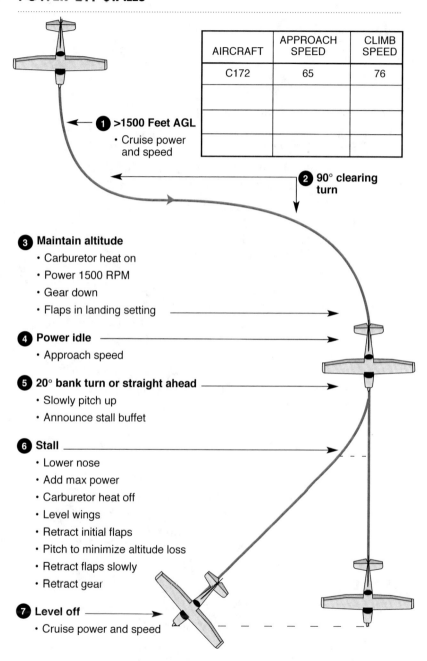

AIRCRAFT	APPROACH SPEED	CLIMB SPEED
C172	65	76

1 **>1500 Feet AGL**
- Cruise power and speed

2 **90° clearing turn**

3 **Maintain altitude**
- Carburetor heat on
- Power 1500 RPM
- Gear down
- Flaps in landing setting

4 **Power idle**
- Approach speed

5 **20° bank turn or straight ahead**
- Slowly pitch up
- Announce stall buffet

6 **Stall**
- Lower nose
- Add max power
- Carburetor heat off
- Level wings
- Retract initial flaps
- Pitch to minimize altitude loss
- Retract flaps slowly
- Retract gear

7 **Level off**
- Cruise power and speed

Limitations — Completes task above 1,500 Feet AGL
Maintains heading ±10° •Maintains bank angle ±10°

POWER-ON STALLS

OBJECTIVE

To teach the private student the knowledge of the elements related to power-on stalls.

COMPLETION STANDARDS

1. Selects an entry altitude that will allow the task to be completed no lower than 1,500 feet (460 meters) AGL.
2. Establishes the takeoff or departure configuration. Sets power to no less than 65 percent available power.
3. Transitions smoothly from the takeoff or departure attitude to the pitch attitude that will induce a stall.
4. Maintains a specified heading, ±10°, if in straight flight; maintains a specified angle of bank not to exceed 20°, ±10°, if in turning flight, while inducing the stall.
5. Recognizes and recovers promptly after the stall occurs by simultaneously reducing the angle of attack, increasing power as appropriate, and leveling the wings to return to a straight-and-level flight attitude with a minimum loss of altitude appropriate for the airplane.
6. Retracts the flaps to the recommended setting; retracts the landing gear, if retractable, after a positive rate of climb is established.
7. Accelerates to V_X or V_Y before the final flap retraction; returns to the altitude, heading, and airspeed specified by the examiner.

DESCRIPTION

The airplane is stabilized during entry at the airspeed, configuration, and power setting appropriate to takeoff and departure. The pitch attitude is then raised that will induce a full stall. Recovery is initiated promptly after the full stall.

PROCEDURE

1. Clear the area.
2. After completing the clearing turns, apply carburetor heat and reduce power to 1,500 RPM.
3. Maintain heading and altitude while slowing to rotation speed.

4. Once airspeed is in the flap operating range, lower flaps to the takeoff setting and lower landing gear (or as directed).

5. Once rotation speed is obtained, simultaneously increase pitch to stall attitude and apply takeoff power or a power setting so as not to exceed excessively high pitch attitudes (30° or more nose up).

6. Carburetor heat off.

7. For turning stalls, establish a 20° bank in either direction.

8. Continue increasing the pitch attitude, announcing any buffeting, until a full stall occurs.

9. Initiate recovery by lowering nose to decrease angle of attack while using coordinated aileron and rudder to level the wings.

10. Increase power or verify power is at maximum available.

11. Adjust pitch to minimize altitude loss.

12. Once a positive recovery is assured, slowly raise flaps, landing gear (if extended) and accelerate to cruise speed.

References

Private Pilot Practical Test Standards FAA-S-8081-14A, pg. 1-28.
Airplane Flying Handbook FAA-H-8083-3, pg. 4-8, 4-9.
Stall and Spin Awareness Training AC 61-67.
Pilot Operating Handbook/Approved Flight Manual.

POWER-ON STALLS

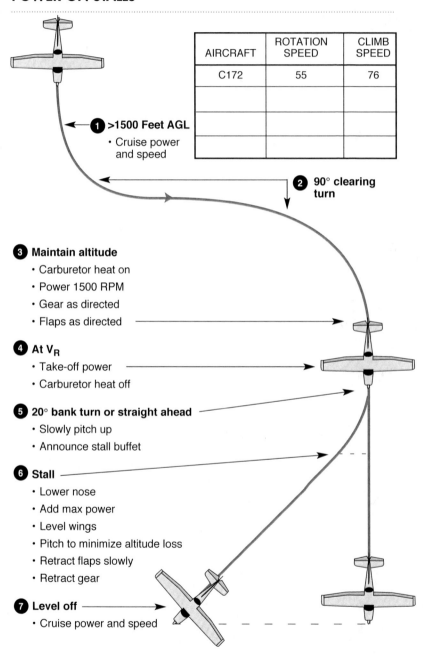

AIRCRAFT	ROTATION SPEED	CLIMB SPEED
C172	55	76

1 **>1500 Feet AGL**
- Cruise power and speed

2 **90° clearing turn**

3 **Maintain altitude**
- Carburetor heat on
- Power 1500 RPM
- Gear as directed
- Flaps as directed

4 **At V_R**
- Take-off power
- Carburetor heat off

5 **20° bank turn or straight ahead**
- Slowly pitch up
- Announce stall buffet

6 **Stall**
- Lower nose
- Add max power
- Level wings
- Pitch to minimize altitude loss
- Retract flaps slowly
- Retract gear

7 **Level off**
- Cruise power and speed

Limitations —Completes task above 1,500 Feet AGL
Maintains heading ±10° * Maintains bank angle ±10°

CHAPTER EIGHT
BASIC INSTRUMENT
MANEUVERS

STRAIGHT-AND-LEVEL FLIGHT

OBJECTIVE

To teach the private student the knowledge of the elements related to attitude instrument flying during straight-and-level flight.

COMPLETION STANDARDS

1. Maintains straight-and-level flight solely by reference to instruments using proper instrument cross-check and interpretation, and coordinated control application.
2. Maintains altitude, ± 200 feet (60 meters); heading, ±20°; and airspeed, ±10 knots.

DESCRIPTION

With reference to flight instruments only, altitude, heading and airspeed are maintained utilizing proper scan, interpretation and airplane control techniques.

PROCEDURE

1. Establish the attitude for straight and level flight by reference to the attitude indicator, then set power for the desired airspeed by reference to the tachometer and/or MP (Manifold Pressure) gages.
2. As the airplane stabilizes, adjust trim to relieve all control pressures.
3. Continue scanning of all instruments, using altimeter as primary instrument for pitch, airspeed as primary for power, and heading indicator as primary for bank.
4. Interpret the instruments to determine if minor adjustments are required. Decide how the adjustments, if needed, are to be made.
5. Apply the proper control of pitch, power or bank as needed.
   a. For altitude errors of less than 100 feet on the altimeter, correct using 1/2 bar width on the attitude indicator. (The bar refers to the miniature airplane's wings.)
   b. For altitude errors of more than 100 feet on the altimeter, correct them by using an initial full bar width correction on the attitude indicator. Vertical Speed Indicator (VSI) rate of return should be twice the amount of altitude the

airplane is off. So, if you are off 200 feet, you should use a VSI rate of 400 fpm.

c. For heading errors, make your correction to the desired heading by using a bank angle half the number of degrees to be turned, not to exceed standard rate.

d. For airspeed errors, adjust power 100 RPM/1" MP for each five knots of airspeed. Let the airplane stabilize and trim off control pressures.

6. Continue scanning of all instruments noting how the supporting instruments can aid in your interpretation and subsequent control.

7. Repeat steps 2 through 6.

References
Private Pilot Practical Test Standards FAA-S-8081-14A, pg. 1-29.
Airplane Flying Handbook FAA-H-8083-3. pg 16-12 ⇒ 16-17.
Instrument Flying Handbook FAA-H-8083-15, pg. 5-1 ⇒ 5-15.

STRAIGHT AND LEVEL FLIGHT

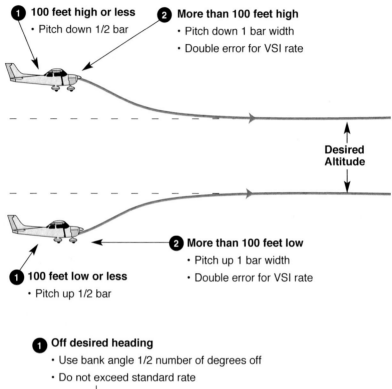

1 100 feet high or less
- Pitch down 1/2 bar

2 More than 100 feet high
- Pitch down 1 bar width
- Double error for VSI rate

Desired
Altitude

2 More than 100 feet low
- Pitch up 1 bar width
- Double error for VSI rate

1 100 feet low or less
- Pitch up 1/2 bar

1 Off desired heading
- Use bank angle 1/2 number of degrees off
- Do not exceed standard rate

1 Off desired airspeed
- Adjust 100 RPM/1" MP per 5 knots

Desired
Heading

PRIMARY			SUPPORTING		
PITCH	POWER	BANK	PITCH	POWER	BANK
ALT	AS	HI	AI/VSI	RPM/MP	TC/AI

Limitations — Heading ±20° • Altitude ±200 Feet • Airspeed ±10 knots

CONSTANT AIRSPEED CLIMBS

OBJECTIVE

To teach the private student the knowledge of the elements related to attitude instrument flying during constant airspeed climbs.

COMPLETION STANDARDS

1. Establishes the climb configuration specified by the examiner.
2. Transitions to the climb pitch attitude and power setting on an assigned heading using proper instrument cross-check and interpretation, and coordinated control application.
3. Demonstrates climbs solely by reference to instruments at a constant airspeed to specific altitudes in straight flight and turns.
4. Levels off at the assigned altitude and maintains that altitude, ±200 feet (60 meters); maintains heading, ±20°; maintains airspeed, ±10 knots.

DESCRIPTION

With reference to flight instruments only, a constant airspeed is maintained during a climb at a fixed power setting by establishing and maintaining an appropriate pitch attitude.

PROCEDURE

1. Establish the approximate climb attitude for the predetermined airspeed using the attitude indicator. Primary flight instruments are: Attitude Indicator (AI)-pitch, Heading Indicator (HI)-bank, and RPM/MP-power.
2. When airspeed is within five knots of desired, set power smoothly as required.
3. Use throttle position, engine sound and control pressures to estimate the initial power setting. Include the RPM/MP gauge in your cross-check when final adjustment is made. During the transition the RPM/MP is primary for power.
4. Avoid fixating on the RPM/MP gauge.
5. Continue scanning all instruments and maintain pitch until airspeed is stabilized. Trim off pressures.
6. Primary instrument for pitch is now the airspeed indicator. Other primary instruments remain the same.

7. Interpret the instruments to determine if minor adjustments are required. Decide how the adjustments are to be made.

8. Apply the proper control of pitch, power or bank as needed. Let the airplane stabilize and trim off control pressures.

9. Continue to scan all instruments noting how the supporting instruments aid in your interpretation and subsequent control.

10. Repeat steps 6 through 9.

11. Lead level off by 10% of the rate of climb. Pitch to level using the attitude indicator for the transition. Altimeter is now primary for pitch. Allow airspeed to increase to the desired speed, smoothly reduce power to a predetermined setting for the desired speed, and trim off the control pressures.

References

Private Pilot Practical Test Standards FAA-S-8081-14A, pg. 1-29.
Airplane Flying Handbook FAA-H-8083-3. pg 16-12 ⇒ 16-17.
Instrument Flying Handbook FAA-H-8083-15, pg. 5-16 ⇒ 5-22.

CONSTANT AIRSPEED CLIMBS

> ### Rules of Thumb
>
> - **100 RPM/1" MP = 5 knots**
> - **Lead level off by 10% of VSI**
> - **Lead roll out by 1/2 bank angle**

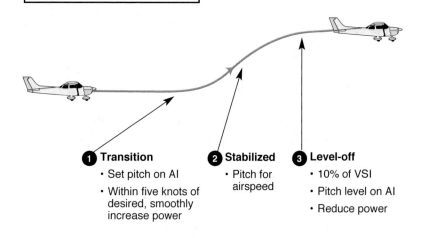

1 Transition
- Set pitch on AI
- Within five knots of desired, smoothly increase power

2 Stabilized
- Pitch for airspeed

3 Level-off
- 10% of VSI
- Pitch level on AI
- Reduce power

A/C	V_X			V_Y			CRUISE CLIMB		
	AS	POWER	PITCH	AS	POWER	PITCH	AS	POWER	PITCH
C172	61	FULL	+9°	75	FULL	+6°	85	FULL	+4°

	PRIMARY			SUPPORTING		
	PITCH	POWER	BANK	PITCH	POWER	BANK
TRANSITION	AI	RPM/MP	HI	ALT/VSI	AS	TC/AI
STABILIZED	AS	RPM/MP	HI	ALT/AI	VSI	TC/AI

Limitations — Heading ±20° • Altitude ±200 Feet • Airspeed ± 10 Knots

CONSTANT AIRSPEED DESCENTS

OBJECTIVE

To teach the private student the knowledge of the elements related to attitude instrument flying during straight, constant airspeed descents.

COMPLETION STANDARDS

1. Establishes the descent configuration specified by the examiner.
2. Transitions to the descent pitch attitude and power setting on an assigned heading using proper instrument cross-check and interpretation, and coordinated control application.
3. Demonstrates descents solely by reference to instruments at a constant airspeed to specific altitudes in straight flight and turns
4. Levels off at the assigned altitude and maintains that altitude, ±200 feet (60 meters); maintains heading, ±20°; maintains airspeed, ±10 knots.

DESCRIPTION

With reference to flight instruments only, a constant airspeed is maintained during a descent at a fixed power setting by establishing and maintaining an appropriate pitch attitude.

PROCEDURE

1. Smoothly reduce power to a predetermined power setting.
2. Use throttle position, engine sound and control pressures to estimate the initial power setting. Include the RPM/MP gauge in your cross-check when final adjustment is made. During the transition the RPM/MP is primary for power.
3. Avoid fixating on the RPM/MP gauge.
4. Maintain level flight until the airspeed decreases to desired descent airspeed.
5. Pitch to the descent attitude using the attitude indicator as required to maintain the desired airspeed. Primary instruments are: Attitude Indicator (AI)-pitch, Heading Indicator (HI)-bank, RPM/MP-power.
6. Continue scanning and maintain pitch until airspeed is stabilized. Trim off pressures.

7. Primary instrument for pitch is now the airspeed indicator. Other primary instruments remain the same.

8. Interpret the instruments to determine if minor adjustments are required. Decide how the adjustments are to be made.

9. Apply the proper control of pitch, power or bank as needed. Let the airplane stabilize and trim.

10. Continue to scan all instruments, noting how the supporting instruments aid in your interpretation and subsequent control.

11. Repeat steps 7 through 10.

12. Lead level off by 10% of the rate of descent. Pitch to level using the attitude indicator for the transition. Altimeter is now primary for pitch.

13. Simultaneously adjust pitch attitude to level flight and smoothly add power to a predetermined setting that will hold the airspeed constant. Trim off pressures.

References

Private Pilot Practical Test Standards FAA-S-8081-14A, pg. 1-30.
Airplane Flying Handbook FAA-H-8083-3. pg 16-12 ⇒ 16-17.
Instrument Flying Handbook FAA-H-8083-15, pg. 5-16 ⇒ 5-22.

CONSTANT AIRSPEED DESCENTS

Rules of Thumb
• 100 RPM/1" MP = 5 knots • Lead level off by 10% of VSI • Lead roll out by 1/2 bank angle

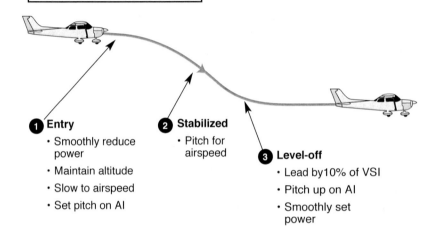

1 Entry
- Smoothly reduce power
- Maintain altitude
- Slow to airspeed
- Set pitch on AI

2 Stabilized
- Pitch for airspeed

3 Level-off
- Lead by 10% of VSI
- Pitch up on AI
- Smoothly set power

A/C	HIGH			NORMAL			LOW		
	AS	POWER	PITCH	AS	POWER	PITCH	AS	POWER	PITCH
C172	105	2000	-3°	90	1700	-3°	75	1400	-4°

	PRIMARY			SUPPORTING		
	PITCH	POWER	BANK	PITCH	POWER	BANK
TRANSITION	AI	RPM/MP	HI	ALT/VSI	AS	TC/AI
STABILIZED	AS	RPM/MP	HI	ALT/AI	VSI	TC/AI

Limitations — Heading ±20° • Level-off ±200 Feet • Airspeed ±10 Knots

TURNS TO HEADINGS

OBJECTIVE

To teach the private student the knowledge of the elements related to attitude instrument flying during turns to headings.

COMPLETION STANDARDS

1. Transitions to the level-turn attitude using proper instrument cross-check and interpretation, and coordinated control application.
2. Demonstrates turns to headings solely by reference to instruments; maintains altitude, ±200 feet (60 meters); maintains a standard rate turn and rolls out on the assigned heading, ±10°; maintains airspeed, ±10 knots.

DESCRIPTION

With reference to flight instruments only, turns made at standard rate using the turn coordinator as reference for bank.

PROCEDURE

1. Maintain the airplane in straight-and-level. Determine shortest direction to new heading.(left/right)
2. Roll in using the attitude indicator to establish the approximate angle of bank.
   Bank angle standard rate = (TAS/10) x 1.5
   Example: (100/10) x 1.5 = 15°
3. Once established, check the turn coordinator, now primary for bank, for a standard rate turn indication.
4. Adjust bank as necessary to maintain a standard rate turn.
5. Maintain coordinated flight.
6. Altimeter is primary for pitch, and airspeed is primary for power.
7. Interpret the instruments to determine if minor adjustments are required. Decide how the adjustments are to be made.
8. Apply the proper control of pitch, power or bank as needed. Let the airplane stabilize and trim.
9. Continue to scan all instruments, noting how the supporting instruments aid in your interpretation and subsequent control.

10. Repeat steps four through nine.

11. Lead roll out on your heading indicator by 1/2 your bank angle. Roll out using the attitude indicator for the transition.

12. Adjust pitch attitude and power as necessary to maintain altitude and airspeed, then trim off the pressures.

Note: If the airplane has a turn and slip indicator, the phrase "turn coordinator" applies to the turn needle.

References
Private Pilot Practical Test Standards FAA-S-8081-14A, pg. 1-30.
Airplane Flying Handbook FAA-H-8083-3. pg 16-12 ⟹ 16-17.
Instrument Flying Handbook FAA-H-8083-15, pg. 5-22 ⟹ 5-30.

TURNS TO HEADINGS

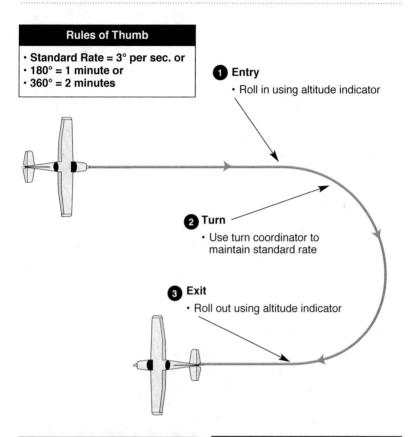

Rules of Thumb

- **Standard Rate = 3° per sec. or**
- **180° = 1 minute or**
- **360° = 2 minutes**

1 **Entry**
 - Roll in using altitude indicator

2 **Turn**
 - Use turn coordinator to maintain standard rate

3 **Exit**
 - Roll out using altitude indicator

Formula
Bank angle for standard rate $= (TAS/10) \times 1.5$

	STANDARD RATE			
A/C	BANK	TAS	POWER	PITCH
C172	14°	90	2200	0°

	PRIMARY			SECONDARY		
	PITCH	POWER	BANK	PITCH	POWER	BANK
TRANSITION	ALT	AS	AI	AI/VSI	RPM/MP	TC/HI
STABILIZED	ALT	AS	TC	AI/VSI	RPM/MP	AI/HI

Limitations — Altitude ±200 feet • Airspeed ±10 knots
Maintains standard rate • Rolls out on specified heading ±20°

RECOVERY FROM UNUSUAL FLIGHT ATTITUDES

OBJECTIVE

To teach the private student the knowledge of the elements related to attitude instrument flying during unusual attitudes.

COMPLETION STANDARDS

1. Recognizes unusual flight attitudes solely by reference to instruments, recovers promptly to a stabilized level flight attitude using proper instrument cross-check and interpretation and smooth, coordinated control application in the correct sequence.

DESCRIPTION

While simulating emergency instrument conditions, the instructor/examiner will force the airplane to a critical flight attitude. When instructed, the student will take control of the airplane and recover to straight and level flight.

PROCEDURE

1. Note the original heading and altitude.
2. Two methods of establishing a critical flight attitude may be used.
   a. The hooded student is told to look down or up, close his/her eyes and place the airplane in a standard rate turn.
   b. The hooded student is told to remove his/her hands and feet from the controls, look down or up and close his /her eyes. The instructor/examiner places the airplane into a critical flight attitude.
3. In either of the above cases, when the airplane is in the critical flight attitude, the instructor/examiner will clearly tell the student to open his/her eyes and recover solely by reference to the instruments.
4. Recognize what type of critical attitude you are experiencing.
5. Interpret the instruments to produce correct control inputs.
6. Two common situations normally occur.
   a. Nose high attitude— airspeed low and decreasing.
      1. Add full power.
      2. Pitch down to level flight.
      3. Level the wings.
      4. Return to original heading and altitude.

b. Nose low attitude— airspeed high and increasing.
  1. Reduce power as required.
  2. Level wings.
  3. Pitch up for level flight.
  4. Return to original heading and altitude.

7. The pitch attitude will be approximately level when the airspeed and altimeter needles stop their movement and the vertical speed indicator reverses its trend.

8. Recover by prompt, smooth, coordinated control, using proper sequence.

9. Avoid excessive load factors, airspeeds or stalls.

10. Do not use the attitude indicator until you verify its reliability. The attitude may tumble if its limits are exceeded.

References
Private Pilot Practical Test Standards FAA-S-8081-14A, pg. 1-30.
Airplane Flying Handbook FAA-H-8083-3. pg 16-12 ⇒ 16-17.
Instrument Flying Handbook FAA-H-8083-15, pg. 5-31 ⇒ 5-33.

CHAPTER TEN
EMERGENCY OPERATIONS
AND POSTFLIGHT
PROCEDURES

EMERGENCY APPROACH AND LANDING (SIMULATED)

OBJECTIVE

To teach the private student the knowledge of the elements related to emergency approach and landing procedures.

COMPLETION STANDARDS

1. Analyzes the situation and selects an appropriate course of action.
2. Establishes and maintains the recommended best-glide airspeed, ±10 knots.
3. Selects a suitable landing area.
4. Plans and follows a flight pattern to the selected landing area considering altitude, wind, terrain, obstructions.
5. Prepares for landing, or go-around, as specified by the examiner.
6. Follows the appropriate checklist.

DESCRIPTION

This procedure consists of maneuvering the airplane with partial or complete power loss so as to land at a predetermined, suitable landing area. During this maneuver an attempt is made to find the reason for the malfunction and follow an appropriate checklist.

PROCEDURE

1. Upon simulated engine failure establish and trim for best-glide speed for airplane weight.
2. Carburetor heat on.
3. Establish the recommended configuration (high altitude)—
   a. flaps up
   b. gear up.
4. Select a suitable landing area within gliding distance and turn toward it.
5. Determine the reason for the power loss (time permitting).
   a. Fuel selector fullest tank or on.
   b. Mixture rich.
   c. Props forward.
   d. Throttle idle then back to mid-range.
   e. Fuel pumps on.
   f. Magneto switch check
   g. Primer in and locked or off.

6. Time permitting, back up the memory items on engine troubleshoot with the checklist.

7. Plan and follow a flight pattern to the selected landing area using one of the following approaches.
   a. 360° approach- greater than 2000 feet and above the landing point.
   b. 180° side approach.
   c. 90° approach.
   d. Straight in approach.

   Take into consideration your altitude, wind, terrain, obstructions and any other factors.

8. Time permitting, advise a controlling agency, (Emergency- 121.5, Tower, FSS, Center.,) of position and nature of emergency, color of airplane, and the number of passengers (simulate).

9. Squawk 7700 on transponder (simulate).

10. Maneuver the airplane to the downwind key position, a position abeam the landing point, at the normal traffic pattern altitude appropriate to the landing site. (1000 to 1200 feet above ground.)

11. Time permitting, complete "Forced Landing" checklist (simulate) and back it up with the checklist.

12. Lower landing gear at appropriate altitude.

13. At a point when a safe landing is assured, then set flaps as required.

14 Seat belts/shoulder harness' on.

15. Doors ajar.

16. Time permitting, brief passengers on emergency landing procedures and secure all objects in the airplane.

17. Adjust base and/or slip the airplane on final to assure a safe landing at the selected point of touchdown.

Note: Consult the pilots operating handbook for the recommended procedure for "during flight restarts" and "forced landing" checklists.

References
Private Pilot Practical Test Standards FAA-S-8081-14A, pg. 1-32.
Airplane Flying Handbook FAA-H-8083-3, pg. 8-24 8-27.
Aeronautical Information Manual, para. 6--3-1 6-3-3.

AIRCRAFT	SPEED
C172	65

Limitations — Airspeed ±10 knots

AFTER LANDING, PARKING, AND SECURING

OBJECTIVE

To teach the private pilot student the knowledge of the elements related to after landing, parking and securing procedures.

COMPLETION STANDARDS

1. Maintains directional control after touchdown while decelerating to an appropriate speed.
2. Observes runway hold lines and other surface control markings and lighting.
3. Parks in an appropriate area, considering the safety of nearby persons and property.
4. Follows the appropriate procedure for engine shutdown.
5. Completes the appropriate checklist.
6. Conducts an appropriate postflight inspection and secures the aircraft.

PROCEDURE

1. Slow to normal taxi speed and clear the runway.
2. Clear of runway, complete after landing checklist.
3. Obtain taxi clearance if necessary.
4. Park aircraft in an area considering prop blast and winds.
5. Set parking brake.
6. Test ignition grounding system by momentarily turning ignition to off and the engine should begin to shut down.
7. All electrical systems off. (except master)
8. Mixture to idle cuttoff.
9. After engine stops, ignition off and master electrical off.
10. Complete shutdown checklists.
11. Install control locks and tie down aircraft.
12. Conduct exterior postflight walk around checking condition of aircraft.

References

Private Pilot Practical Test Standards FAA-S-8081-14A, pg. 1-35.
Airplane Flying Handbook FAA-H-8083-3, pg. 2-11, 2-12.
Pilot Operating Handbook/Approved Flight Manual.

APPENDIX

ABBREVIATIONS

AC ....Advisory Circular
ADF ....Automatic Direction Finder
AF/D ....Airport Facilities Directory
AFM..Approved Flight Manual
AGL..Above Ground Level
AI ....Attitude Indicator
ALT ....Altimeter
ATC ....Air-route Traffic Control
ATIS ....Automatic Terminal Information Service
AS..Airspeed
CDI ....Course Deviation Indicator
DME..Distance Measuring Equipment
ETA ....Estimated Time Arrival
ETE ....Estimated Time Enroute
FPM ....Feet Per Minute
FSS ....Flight Service Station
GPH..Gallons Per Hour
GPS ....Global Positioning System
GS ....Groundspeed
HI ....Heading Indicator
MCA..Minimum Controllable Airspeed
MHz..Mega Hertz
MP..Manifold Pressure
NDB ....Non Directional Beacon
NOTAMs ....Notices to Airmen
OBS..Omni Bearing Selector
POH ....Pilot Operating Handbook
PPH..Pounds Per Hour
RPM ....Revolutions Per Minute
TAS ....True Airspeed
TC..Turn Coordinator
TPA ....Traffic Pattern Altitude
VFR..Visual Flight Rules
VOR..................................Very high frequency Omnirange station
VORTAC ....ultra high frequency tactical air navigation aid
V_R ....Rotation Airspeed
V_{S1}..Stall Speed in a Specific Configuration
V_{S0}..Stall Speed in the Landing Configuration
V_X ....Best Angle of Climb Speed
VY ....Best Rate of Climb Speed

WEIGHT AND BALANCE

	WEIGHT	C.G.	MOMENT
EMPTY WEIGHT			
PILOT/FRONT PASS			
BACK PASS			
BACK PASS			
CARGO 1			
CARGO 2			
ZERO FUEL WEIGHT			
FUEL			
RAMP WEIGHT			
START/TAXI/TAKEOFF			
TAKEOFF WEIGHT			
FUEL BURN			
LANDING WEIGHT			

PERFORMANCE

TEMPERATURE _____   ALTIMETER _____

WINDS_____ V_A _____

PRESSURE ALT _____   DENSITY ALT_____

TAKEOFF DISTANCE/OVER 50 FOOT _____/ _____

ROTATION SPEED/CLIMB OUT SPEED _____/ _____

LANDING DISTANCE/OVER 50 FOOT_____/ _____

LANDING SPEED _____

ATIS

CODE/TIME_____WIND_____

VISIBILITY_____

SKY_____FEW_____SCT_____BKN_____OVC

TEMPERATURE_____DEW POINT_____

ALTIMETER_____RUNWAY_____

NOTAMS/NOTES_____

_____.

_____

CLEARANCE

_____

_____

_____

_____

_____

_____

_____

DIVERSION CHECKLIST

DETERMINE SUITABLE ALTERNATE:

TIME:

POSITION - MARK ON SECTIONAL

MEASURE NEW HEADING: (RESET HI)

DISTANCE:

WINDS ALOFT: GROUNDSPEED:

ETE: ETA:

FUEL BURN:

ALTITUDE CHANGE IF NECESSARY:

UPDATE FLIGHT PLAN WITH FSS

USE ALL THREE TO FIND ALTERNATE

PILOTAGE
DEAD RECKONING
RADIO NAVIGATION

AERO TECH
PUBLICATIONS